M208 Pure

The Open University

AA2

Sequences

This publication forms part of an Open University course. Details of this and other Open University courses can be obtained from the Student Registration and Enquiry Service, The Open University, PO Box 197, Milton Keynes, MK7 6BJ, United Kingdom: tel. +44 (0)870 300 6090, e-mail general-enquiries@open.ac.uk

Alternatively, you may visit the Open University website at http://www.open.ac.uk where you can learn more about the wide range of courses and packs offered at all levels by The Open University.

To purchase a selection of Open University course materials, visit http://www.ouw.co.uk, or contact Open University Worldwide, Michael Young Building, Walton Hall, Milton Keynes, MK7 6AA, United Kingdom, for a brochure: tel. +44 (0)1908 858793, fax +44 (0)1908 858787, e-mail ouw-customer-services@open.ac.uk

The Open University, Walton Hall, Milton Keynes, MK7 6AA.

First published 2006. Reprinted with amendments 2007.

Edited, designed and typeset by The Open University, using the Open University TEX System.

Printed and bound in the United Kingdom by Hobbs the Printers Limited, Brunel Road, Totton, Hampshire SO40 3WX.

ISBN 0 7492 0208 4

1.2

Contents

Introduction   **4**

1   Introducing sequences   **5**
1.1   What is a sequence?   5
1.2   Monotonic sequences   6

2   Null sequences   **10**
2.1   What is a null sequence? (audio section)   10
2.2   Properties of null sequences   18

3   Convergent sequences   **22**
3.1   What is a convergent sequence?   22
3.2   Combination Rules for convergent sequences   23
3.3   Further rules for convergent sequences   27

4   Divergent sequences   **30**
4.1   What is a divergent sequence?   30
4.2   Bounded and unbounded sequences   30
4.3   Sequences tending to infinity   32
4.4   Subsequences   35

5   Monotone Convergence Theorem   **38**
5.1   Monotonic sequences (video section)   38
5.2   Review of the video programme   40
5.3   Post-programme work   44

Solutions to the exercises   **45**

Index   **53**

Introduction

This unit deals with sequences of real numbers, such as

$$1, \tfrac{1}{2}, \tfrac{1}{3}, \tfrac{1}{4}, \tfrac{1}{5}, \tfrac{1}{6}, \ldots,$$

$$0, 1, 0, 1, 0, 1, \ldots,$$

$$1, 2, 4, 8, 16, 32, \ldots.$$

The three dots (an ellipsis) indicate that the sequence continues indefinitely.

It describes in detail various properties that a sequence may possess, the most important of which is *convergence*. Roughly speaking, a sequence is *convergent*, or *tends to a limit*, if the numbers, or *terms*, in the sequence approach arbitrarily close to a unique real number, which is called the *limit* of the sequence. For example, we shall see that the sequence

$$1, \tfrac{1}{2}, \tfrac{1}{3}, \tfrac{1}{4}, \tfrac{1}{5}, \tfrac{1}{6}, \ldots,$$

is convergent with limit 0. On the other hand, the terms of the sequence

$$0, 1, 0, 1, 0, 1, \ldots,$$

do not approach arbitrarily close to a unique real number, so this sequence is not convergent. Likewise, the sequence

$$1, 2, 4, 8, 16, 32, \ldots,$$

is not convergent. A sequence which is not convergent is called *divergent*.

Intuitively, it seems plausible that some sequences are convergent, whereas others are not. However, the above description of convergence, involving the phrase 'approach arbitrarily close to', lacks the precision required in pure mathematics. If we wish to work in a serious way with convergent sequences, prove results about them and decide beyond doubt whether or not a given sequence is convergent, then we need a rigorous definition of this concept.

Historically, such a definition emerged only in the late nineteenth century, when mathematicians such as Bolzano, Cantor, Cauchy, Dedekind and Weierstrass placed analysis on a rigorous footing. It is not surprising, therefore, that at first sight the definition of convergence is rather subtle and it may take you a little time to grasp it fully.

In Section 1 we show how to picture the behaviour of a sequence by drawing a *sequence diagram*. We also introduce *monotonic* sequences, that is, sequences which are either increasing or decreasing.

In Section 2 we explain (in the audio section) the definition of a *null* sequence, that is, a convergent sequence with limit 0. We then prove various properties of null sequences and list some basic null sequences.

In Section 3 we discuss general convergent sequences (those which converge, but do not necessarily have limit 0), together with techniques for calculating their limits.

In Section 4 we study divergent sequences, giving particular emphasis to sequences which tend to infinity or to minus infinity. We also show that convergent sequences are bounded; it follows that unbounded sequences are necessarily divergent.

Finally, in Section 5, we prove the Monotone Convergence Theorem. This states that any increasing sequence which is bounded above must be convergent. Then, in the video programme, we illustrate this theorem with particular sequences which converge to π and e.

Study guide

It is important to study the sections in numerical order and you should spend most of your study time on Sections 2–4. The video associated with Section 5 can be watched after studying Sections 1–3 and Subsection 5.1, if you wish.

1   Introducing sequences

After working through this section, you should be able to:

(a) draw the *sequence diagram* of a given sequence;
(b) explain what is meant by a *monotonic* sequence;
(c) explain the meaning of the phrase 'a sequence *eventually* has a given property'.

1.1 What is a sequence?

Ever since learning to count, you have been familiar with the sequence of natural numbers

$$1, 2, 3, 4, 5, 6, \ldots.$$

You have also encountered many other sequences of numbers, such as

$$2, 4, 6, 8, 10, 12, \ldots,$$
$$\tfrac{1}{2}, \tfrac{1}{4}, \tfrac{1}{8}, \tfrac{1}{16}, \tfrac{1}{32}, \tfrac{1}{64}, \ldots.$$

We begin our study of sequences with a definition and some notation.

Definition   A **sequence** is an unending list of real numbers

$$a_1, a_2, a_3, \ldots.$$

The real number a_n is called the **nth term** of the sequence, and the sequence is denoted by

$$\{a_n\}.$$

Alternative notations are (a_n) and $\langle a_n \rangle$.

In each of the sequences above, we wrote down the first few terms and left you to assume that subsequent terms are obtained by continuing the pattern in an obvious way. It is usually better, however, to give a precise description of a typical term of a sequence, and we can do this by stating an explicit formula for the nth term. For example, the expression $\{2n - 1\}$ denotes the sequence

$$1, 3, 5, 7, 9, 11, \ldots,$$

and the sequence $\{a_n\}$ defined by the statement

$$a_n = (-1)^n, \quad n = 1, 2, \ldots,$$

has terms

$$a_1 = -1, \ a_2 = 1, \ a_3 = -1, \ a_4 = 1, \ a_5 = -1, \ \ldots.$$

Exercise 1.1

(a) Calculate the first five terms of each of the following sequences.

    (i) $\{3n + 1\}$ (ii) $\{3^{-n}\}$ (iii) $\{(-1)^n n\}$

(b) Calculate the first five terms of each of the following sequences $\{a_n\}$.

    (i) $a_n = n!, \quad n = 1, 2, \ldots.$

    (ii) $a_n = \left(1 + \dfrac{1}{n}\right)^n, \quad n = 1, 2, \ldots.$

In part (b)(ii), give your answers to 2 decimal places.

Sequences often begin with a term corresponding to $n = 1$. Sometimes, however, it is necessary to begin a sequence with some other value of n. We indicate this by writing, for example, $\{a_n\}_3^\infty$ to represent the sequence

For example, the sequence $\{1/(n! - n)\}$ cannot begin with $n = 1$ or 2.

$$a_3, a_4, a_5, \ldots.$$

Sequence diagrams

It is often helpful to picture how a given sequence $\{a_n\}$ behaves by drawing a **sequence diagram**, that is, a graph of the sequence in $\mathbb{R}^2$. To do this, we mark suitable values of n on the x-axis and, for each value of n, we plot the point (n, a_n). For example, here are sequence diagrams for the sequences $\{2n - 1\}$, $\{1/n\}$ and $\{(-1)^n\}$.

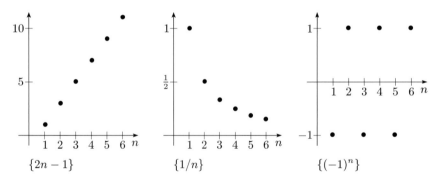

$\{2n - 1\}$ $\{1/n\}$ $\{(-1)^n\}$

In the left-hand graph the points plotted all lie on the straight line $y = 2x - 1$. In the central graph they all lie on the hyperbola $y = 1/x$.

Exercise 1.2   Draw a sequence diagram, showing the first five points, for each of the following sequences.

(a) $\{n^2\}$ (b) $\{3\}$ (c) $\{(1 + 1/n)^n\}$ (d) $\{(-1)^n/n\}$

In part (c), use the solution to Exercise 1.1(b)(ii).

1.2 Monotonic sequences

Many sequences have the property that, as n increases, their terms are either *increasing* or *decreasing*. For example, the sequence $\{2n - 1\}$ has terms $1, 3, 5, 7, \ldots$, which are increasing, whereas the sequence $\{1/n\}$ has terms $1, \frac{1}{2}, \frac{1}{3}, \frac{1}{4}, \ldots$, which are decreasing. The sequence $\{(-1)^n\}$ is neither increasing nor decreasing. All this can be seen clearly on the sequence diagrams.

We now give precise meanings to these words *increasing* and *decreasing*, and introduce the word *monotonic*.

Definition   A sequence $\{a_n\}$ is

constant, if

$$a_{n+1} = a_n, \quad \text{for } n = 1, 2, \ldots;$$

increasing, if

$$a_{n+1} \geq a_n, \quad \text{for } n = 1, 2, \ldots;$$

decreasing, if

$$a_{n+1} \leq a_n, \quad \text{for } n = 1, 2, \ldots;$$

monotonic, if $\{a_n\}$ is either increasing or decreasing.

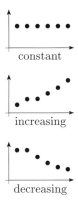

constant

increasing

decreasing

Remarks

1.   For a sequence $\{a_n\}$ to be increasing it is essential that $a_{n+1} \geq a_n$, for *all* $n \geq 1$. However, we do not require strict inequalities because we wish to describe a sequence such as

$$1, 1, 2, 2, 3, 3, 4, 4, \ldots$$

as increasing. One slightly bizarre consequence of the definition is that constant sequences are both increasing and decreasing.

2.   A sequence $\{a_n\}$ is **strictly increasing** if

$$a_{n+1} > a_n, \quad \text{for } n = 1, 2, \ldots,$$

and **strictly decreasing** if

$$a_{n+1} < a_n, \quad \text{for } n = 1, 2, \ldots.$$

To determine whether a sequence is monotonic, it is not sufficient to draw a diagram. There are various ways to prove that a given sequence is monotonic. For example, $1/n$ is (strictly) decreasing because

$$\frac{1}{n+1} < \frac{1}{n}, \quad \text{for } n = 1, 2, \ldots,$$

since $n + 1 > n > 0$, for $n = 1, 2, \ldots.$ Our first example shows some of the other approaches that can be used.

Example 1.1   Determine which of the following sequences $\{a_n\}$ are monotonic.

(a) $a_n = 2n - 1, \quad n = 1, 2, \ldots.$

(b) $a_n = \dfrac{1}{n}, \quad n = 1, 2, \ldots.$

(c) $a_n = (-1)^n, \quad n = 1, 2, \ldots.$

Solution

(a)   We have

$$a_n = 2n - 1 \quad \text{and} \quad a_{n+1} = 2(n + 1) - 1 = 2n + 1,$$

so

$$a_{n+1} - a_n = (2n + 1) - (2n - 1) = 2 \geq 0, \quad \text{for } n = 1, 2, \ldots.$$

It follows that

$$a_{n+1} \geq a_n, \quad \text{for } n = 1, 2, \ldots.$$

Thus $\{2n - 1\}$ is increasing, so $\{2n - 1\}$ is monotonic.

(b) We have

$$a_n = 1/n \quad \text{and} \quad a_{n+1} = 1/(n+1),$$

so

$$\frac{a_{n+1}}{a_n} = \frac{1/(n+1)}{1/n} = \frac{n}{n+1} \leq 1, \quad \text{for } n = 1, 2, \ldots.$$

It follows that

$$a_{n+1} \leq a_n, \quad \text{for } n = 1, 2, \ldots.$$

Thus $\{a_n\}$ is decreasing, so $\{a_n\}$ is monotonic.

(c) The sequence $\{(-1)^n\}$ is not monotonic. Consider the three terms $a_1 = -1$, $a_2 = 1$ and $a_3 = -1$.

We have $a_3 < a_2$, which means that $\{a_n\}$ is not increasing. Also $a_2 > a_1$, which means that $\{a_n\}$ is not decreasing.

Thus $\{(-1)^n\}$ is neither increasing nor decreasing. ■

Example 1.1 illustrates the use of the following two strategies.

Strategy 1.1   To show that a given sequence $\{a_n\}$ is monotonic, consider the difference $a_{n+1} - a_n$.

If $a_{n+1} - a_n \geq 0$, for $n = 1, 2, \ldots$, then $\{a_n\}$ is increasing.

If $a_{n+1} - a_n \leq 0$, for $n = 1, 2, \ldots$, then $\{a_n\}$ is decreasing.

If $a_n > 0$ for all n, then it is often more convenient to use the following strategy.

Strategy 1.2   To show that a given sequence $\{a_n\}$ of *positive* terms is monotonic, consider the quotient $\dfrac{a_{n+1}}{a_n}$.

If $\dfrac{a_{n+1}}{a_n} \geq 1$, for $n = 1, 2, \ldots$, then $\{a_n\}$ is increasing.

If $\dfrac{a_{n+1}}{a_n} \leq 1$, for $n = 1, 2, \ldots$, then $\{a_n\}$ is decreasing.

For a positive sequence, which strategy to use depends on whether you think it is easier to simplify the difference $a_{n+1} - a_n$ or the quotient a_{n+1}/a_n.

Exercise 1.3   Show that the following sequences $\{a_n\}$ are monotonic.

(a) $a_n = n!, \quad n = 1, 2, \ldots.$

(b) $a_n = 2^{-n}, \quad n = 1, 2, \ldots.$

(c) $a_n = n + \dfrac{1}{n}, \quad n = 1, 2, \ldots.$

Often, it is possible to *guess* whether or not a sequence defined by a formula is monotonic, by calculating the first few terms. Consider, for example, the sequence $\{a_n\}$ given by

$$a_n = \left(1 + \frac{1}{n}\right)^n, \quad n = 1, 2, \ldots.$$

In Exercise 1.1(b)(ii) you found that the first five terms of this sequence are approximately

$2, 2.25, 2.37, 2.44, 2.49.$

These terms suggest that the sequence $\{a_n\}$ is increasing and, in fact, it is.

We study this important sequence in detail in the video.

However, the first few terms of a sequence are not always a reliable guide to the sequence's behaviour. Consider, for example, the sequence

$$a_n = \frac{10^n}{n!}, \quad n = 1, 2, \ldots.$$

The first five terms of this sequence are approximately

$10, 50, 167, 417, 833.$

These terms suggest that $\{a_n\}$ is increasing. However, calculation of more terms shows that this is not so, as you can see in this sequence diagram.

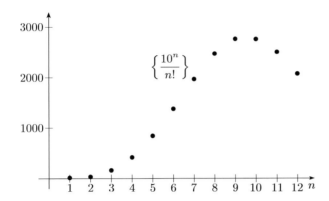

Simplifying a_{n+1}/a_n, we find that

Here we use Strategy 1.2.

$$\frac{a_{n+1}}{a_n} = \frac{10^{n+1}/(n+1)!}{10^n/n!} = \frac{10^{n+1}n!}{10^n(n+1)!} = \frac{10}{n+1}.$$

Since

$$\frac{10}{n+1} \leq 1, \quad \text{for } n = 9, 10, \ldots,$$

we have

$$a_{n+1} \leq a_n, \quad \text{for } n = 9, 10, \ldots.$$

Thus, if we ignore the first eight terms, then $\{a_n\}$ is decreasing.

In fact,
$$a_9 = a_{10},$$
and
$$a_{n+1} < a_n,$$
for $n = 10, 11, \ldots.$

In a situation like this, when a given sequence has a certain property provided that we ignore a finite number of terms, we say that the sequence *eventually* has this property. We have just seen that the sequence $\{10^n/n!\}$ is eventually decreasing.

Another example of this usage is the following:

the terms of the sequence $\{n^2\}$ are eventually greater than 100.

This statement is true because

$$n^2 > 100, \quad \text{for } n > 10.$$

Exercise 1.4   Classify each of the following statements as true or false and justify your answers (if a statement is true, then prove it; if a statement is false, then give a counter-example).

(a) The terms of the sequence $\{2^n\}$ are eventually greater than 1000.

(b) The terms of the sequence $\{(-1)^n\}$ are eventually positive.

(c) The terms of the sequence $\{1/n\}$ are eventually less than 0.025.

(d) The sequence $\{n^4/4^n\}$ is eventually decreasing.

To show that a sequence does *not* eventually have a property, you need to find infinitely many terms of the sequence which fail to have the property.

Further exercises

Exercise 1.5   Calculate the first five terms of each of the following sequences and draw a sequence diagram in each case.

(a) $\{n^2 - 4n + 4\}$ (b) $\{(-1)^{n+1}/n!\}$ (c) $\{\sin(\frac{1}{4}n\pi)\}$

Exercise 1.6   Determine which of the following sequences are monotonic.

(a) $\left\{\dfrac{n}{n+1}\right\}$ (b) $\left\{\dfrac{(-1)^n}{n}\right\}$ (c) $\{2^{1/n}\}$

Exercise 1.7   Prove that the following sequences are each eventually monotonic.

(a) $\{5^n/n!\}$ (b) $\{n + 8/n\}$

2   Null sequences

After working through this section, you should be able to:

(a) explain the definition of *null sequence* and apply it in simple cases;

(b) use the Power Rule, the Combination Rules and the Squeeze Rule to test for null sequences;

(c) recognise certain *basic* null sequences.

2.1 What is a null sequence?

The aims of this audio section are to give a precise definition of a *null sequence* (that is, a sequence which converges to 0) and to introduce some properties of null sequences.

In this section we frequently use the rules for rearranging inequalities. You may find it helpful to revise these rules at this point.

See Unit AA1, Section 2.

We also use the following inequalities, which were proved earlier.

See Frames 4 and 6 of Unit AA1 audio.

$$2^n \geq 1 + n \geq n, \quad \text{for } n = 1, 2, \ldots,$$

and

$$2^n \geq n^2, \quad \text{for } n \geq 4.$$

You should begin by trying the following two exercises; the solutions are given in Frames 1 and 2.

Exercise 2.1   For each of the following statements, find a positive integer N such that the statement is true.

(a) $\dfrac{1}{n} < \dfrac{1}{100}$, for all $n > N$.   (b) $\dfrac{1}{n} < \dfrac{3}{1000}$, for all $n > N$.

Exercise 2.2   For each of the following statements, find a positive integer N such that the statement is true.

(a) $\left| \dfrac{(-1)^n}{n^2} \right| < \dfrac{1}{100}$, for $n > N$.   (b) $\left| \dfrac{(-1)^n}{n^2} \right| < \dfrac{3}{1000}$, for $n > N$.

Listen to the audio as you work through the frames.

Audio

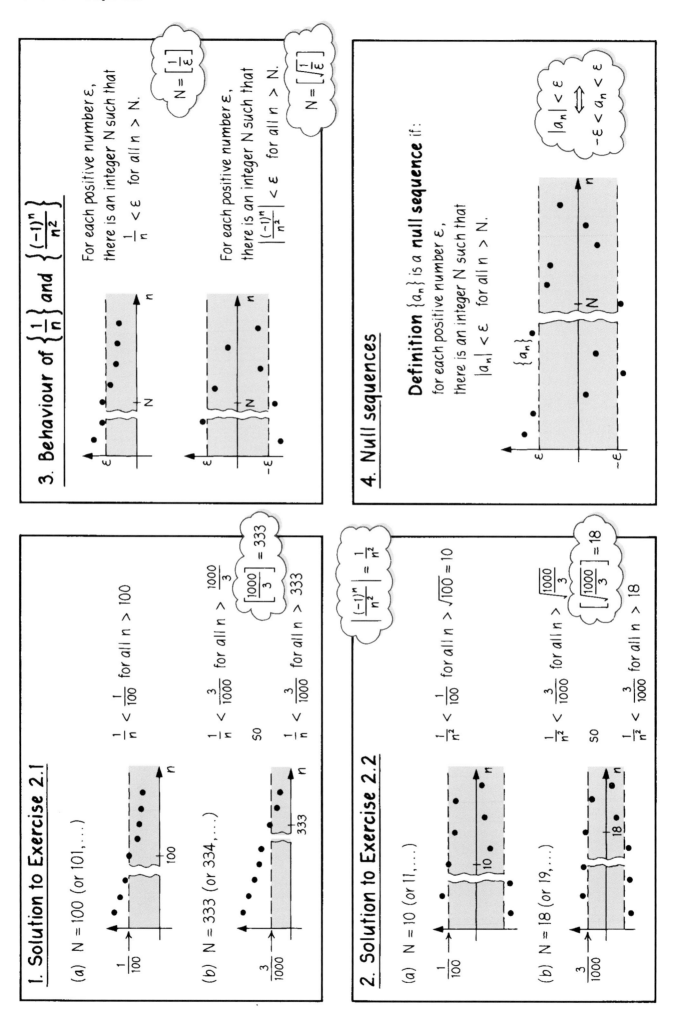

3. Behaviour of $\left\{\dfrac{1}{n}\right\}$ and $\left\{\dfrac{(-1)^n}{n^2}\right\}$

For each positive number ε, there is an integer N such that
$$\frac{1}{n} < \varepsilon \quad \text{for all } n > N.$$

$$N = \left[\frac{1}{\varepsilon}\right]$$

For each positive number ε, there is an integer N such that
$$\left|\frac{(-1)^n}{n^2}\right| < \varepsilon \quad \text{for all } n > N.$$

$$N = \left[\sqrt{\frac{1}{\varepsilon}}\right]$$

4. Null sequences

Definition $\{a_n\}$ is a **null sequence** if:

for each positive number ε,
there is an integer N such that
$$|a_n| < \varepsilon \quad \text{for all } n > N.$$

$$|a_n| < \varepsilon \iff -\varepsilon < a_n < \varepsilon$$

1. Solution to Exercise 2.1

(a) $N = 100$ (or 101,....)

$$\frac{1}{n} < \frac{1}{100} \quad \text{for all } n > 100$$

(b) $N = 333$ (or 334,....)

$$\frac{1}{n} < \frac{3}{1000} \quad \text{for all } n > \frac{1000}{3}$$

so

$$\frac{1}{n} < \frac{3}{1000} \quad \text{for all } n > 333$$

$$\left[\frac{1000}{3}\right] = 333$$

2. Solution to Exercise 2.2

$$\left|\frac{(-1)^n}{n^2}\right| = \frac{1}{n^2}$$

(a) $N = 10$ (or 11,....)

$$\frac{1}{n^2} < \frac{1}{100} \quad \text{for all } n > \sqrt{100} = 10$$

(b) $N = 18$ (or 19,....)

$$\frac{1}{n^2} < \frac{3}{1000} \quad \text{for all } n > \sqrt{\frac{1000}{3}}$$

so

$$\frac{1}{n^2} < \frac{3}{1000} \quad \text{for all } n > 18$$

$$\left[\sqrt{\frac{1000}{3}}\right] = 18$$

5. Is $\left\{\dfrac{1}{n^3}\right\}$ null?

Surely YES?

Given ε, how do we find N?

WANT for each $\varepsilon > 0$, there is an integer N such that
$$\dfrac{1}{n^3} < \varepsilon \quad \text{for all } n > N. \qquad (*)$$

KNOW $\dfrac{1}{n^3} < \varepsilon \iff n^3 > \dfrac{1}{\varepsilon} \iff n > \sqrt[3]{\dfrac{1}{\varepsilon}}$

HENCE if we take $N = \left[\sqrt[3]{\dfrac{1}{\varepsilon}}\right]$, then $(*)$ holds.

RESULT $\left\{\dfrac{1}{n^3}\right\}$ is null.

6. What about $a_n = \begin{cases} 1, & n \text{ odd} \\ 0, & n \text{ even} \end{cases}$?

Surely it's NOT null?

ε = 2, N = 1

ε = ½, N = ?

There is NO integer N such that $|a_n| < \dfrac{1}{2}$ for all $n > N$ so $\{a_n\}$ is not null.

7. Strategy 2.1 Null sequences

Is $\{a_n\}$ null?

GUESS behaviour .... **CHECK** definition

GUESS $\{a_n\}$ is null **CHECK** definition HOLDS
Solve $|a_n| < \varepsilon$ to find N depending on ε.   *Frame 5*

GUESS $\{a_n\}$ is not null **CHECK** definition FAILS
Find ONE value of ε for which there is NO integer N   *Frame 6*

8. Exercise 2.3

Use Strategy 2.1 to determine which of the following sequences are null:

(a) $\left\{\dfrac{1}{2n-1}\right\}$ (b) $\left\{\dfrac{(-1)^n}{10}\right\}$ (c) $\left\{\dfrac{(-1)^n}{n^4+1}\right\}$

11. Examples

The following sequences are null:

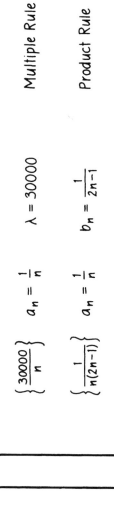

$$\left\{\frac{1}{\sqrt[3]{2n-1}}\right\} \qquad a_n = \frac{1}{2n-1} \qquad p = \frac{1}{3} \qquad \text{Power Rule}$$

$$\left\{\frac{1}{n} + \frac{1}{n^3}\right\} \qquad a_n = \frac{1}{n} \qquad b_n = \frac{1}{n^3} \qquad \text{Sum Rule}$$

$$\left\{\frac{30000}{n}\right\} \qquad a_n = \frac{1}{n} \qquad \lambda = 30000 \qquad \text{Multiple Rule}$$

$$\left\{\frac{1}{n(2n-1)}\right\} \qquad a_n = \frac{1}{n} \qquad b_n = \frac{1}{2n-1} \qquad \text{Product Rule}$$

12. Exercise 2.4

Use the rules to show that the following sequences are null:

(a) $\left\{\dfrac{1}{(2n-1)^3}\right\}$

(b) $\left\{\dfrac{6}{5\sqrt{n}} + \dfrac{5}{(2n-1)^7}\right\}$

(c) $\left\{\dfrac{1}{3n^4(2n-1)^{1/3}}\right\}$

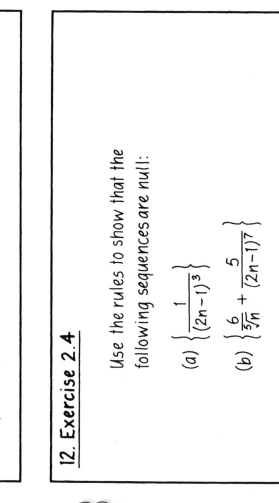

> Assume that $\left\{\dfrac{1}{n}\right\}$ and $\left\{\dfrac{1}{2n-1}\right\}$ are null

9. Is $\left\{\dfrac{1}{\sqrt{n}}\right\}$ null?

> $\left\{\dfrac{1}{n}\right\}$ is null.... and $\dfrac{1}{\sqrt{n}} = \left(\dfrac{1}{n}\right)^{1/2}$

Power Rule

If $\{a_n\}$ is null, where $a_n \geq 0$,

then $\{a_n^p\}$ is null, where $p > 0$.

> $a_n = \dfrac{1}{n} \qquad p = \dfrac{1}{2}$

Hence $\left\{\dfrac{1}{\sqrt{n}}\right\}$ is null.

10. Is $\left\{\dfrac{1}{\sqrt{n}} + \dfrac{1}{2n-1}\right\}$ null?

> $\left\{\dfrac{1}{\sqrt{n}}\right\}$ is null.... ...so is $\dfrac{1}{2n-1}$

Combination Rules

If $\{a_n\}$ and $\{b_n\}$ are null, then so are:

the **sum** $\{a_n + b_n\}$

the **multiple** $\{\lambda a_n\}, \quad \lambda \in \mathbb{R}$

the **product** $\{a_n b_n\}$.

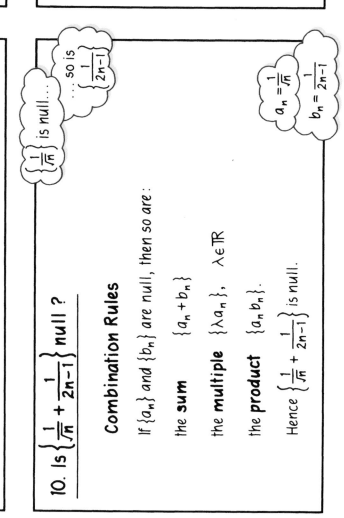

> $a_n = \dfrac{1}{\sqrt{n}} \qquad b_n = \dfrac{1}{2n-1}$

Hence $\left\{\dfrac{1}{\sqrt{n}} + \dfrac{1}{2n-1}\right\}$ is null.

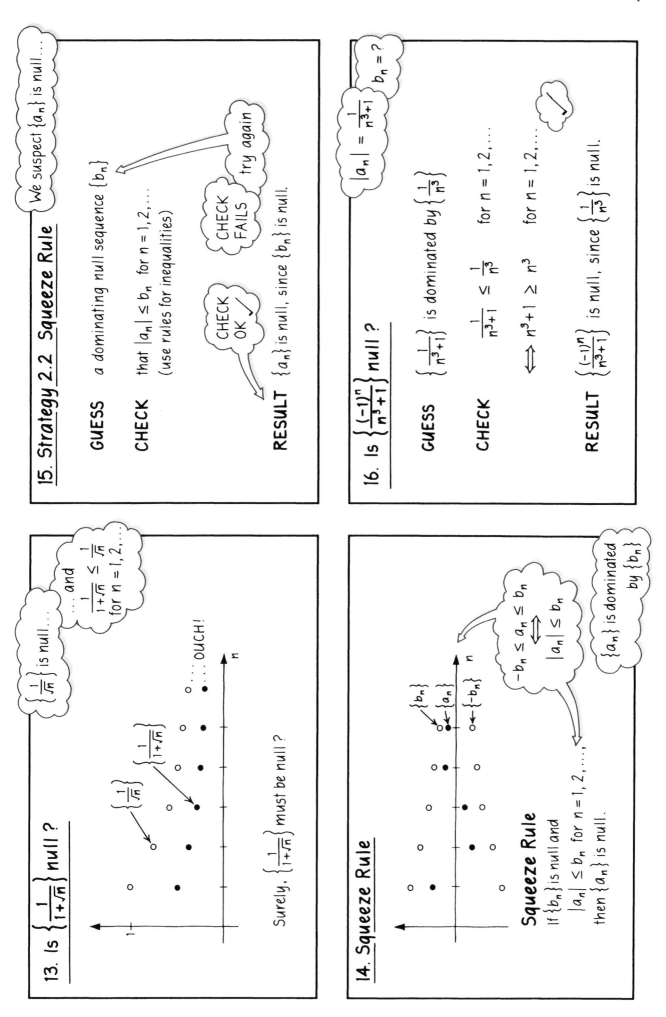

19. Proof of Squeeze Rule

WANT   to show $\{a_n\}$ null; that is,
for each $\epsilon > 0$, there is an integer N such that
$$|a_n| < \epsilon \text{ for all } n > N. \qquad (*)$$

KNOW   (i) $|a_n| \leq b_n$ for $n = 1, 2, \ldots,$ so $b_n \geq 0$.
(ii) $\{b_n\}$ is null, so there is an integer N such that
$$b_n < \epsilon \text{ for all } n > N. \qquad (\dagger)$$

HENCE   if we take N so that $(\dagger)$ holds, then
$$|a_n| \leq b_n < \epsilon \text{ for all } n > N,$$
so $(*)$ also holds.

RESULT $\{a_n\}$ is null.

∎

20. Some harder sequences

$$\left\{ \left(\tfrac{1}{2} \right)^n \right\} ? \quad \left\{ n \left(\tfrac{1}{2} \right)^n \right\} ? \quad \left\{ \tfrac{10^n}{n!} \right\} ?$$

REMEMBER: a finite number of terms *don't matter* :

– it is sufficient to

$\{a_n\}$ is eventually dominated by $\{b_n\}$

CHECK   that $|a_n| \leq b_n$ holds *eventually.*

17. Is $\left\{ \dfrac{2\cos 2n}{n^2} \right\}$ null ?

$$|a_n| = \frac{2|\cos 2n|}{n^2} \qquad b_n = ?$$

GUESS $\left\{ \dfrac{2\cos 2n}{n^2} \right\}$ is dominated by $\left\{ \dfrac{2}{n^2} \right\}$

CHECK $\dfrac{2|\cos 2n|}{n^2} \leq \dfrac{2}{n^2}$ for $n = 1, 2, \ldots$

because

$$|\cos 2n| \leq 1 \text{ for } n = 1, 2, \ldots$$

✓

RESULT $\left\{ \dfrac{2\cos 2n}{n^2} \right\}$ is null, since $\left\{ \dfrac{2}{n^2} \right\}$ is null.

18. Exercise 2.5

Use the Squeeze Rule to show that
the following sequences are null:

(a) $\left\{ \dfrac{1}{n^2 + n} \right\}$ (b) $\left\{ \dfrac{(-1)^n}{n!} \right\}$ (c) $\left\{ \dfrac{\sin n^2}{n^2 + 2^n} \right\}$

21. $\left\{\left(\frac{1}{2}\right)^n\right\}$ is null

(clouds: $a_n = \left(\frac{1}{2}\right)^n = \frac{1}{2^n}$, $b_n = ?$,   ✓ Unit AA1, Frame 4)

GUESS $\left\{\left(\frac{1}{2}\right)^n\right\}$ is dominated by $\left\{\frac{1}{n}\right\}$

CHECK $\dfrac{1}{2^n} \le \dfrac{1}{n}$ for $n = 1, 2, \ldots$

     $\Longleftrightarrow 2^n \ge n$ for $n = 1, 2, \ldots$

RESULT $\left\{\left(\frac{1}{2}\right)^n\right\}$ is null, since $\left\{\frac{1}{n}\right\}$ is null.

$\boxed{\{c^n\} \text{ is null, for } |c| < 1}$

22. $\left\{n\left(\frac{1}{2}\right)^n\right\}$ is null

(clouds: $a_n = \dfrac{n}{2^n}$, $b_n = ?$,   ✓ Unit AA1, Frame 6)

GUESS $\left\{n\left(\frac{1}{2}\right)^n\right\}$ is eventually dominated by $\left\{\frac{1}{n}\right\}$

CHECK $\dfrac{n}{2^n} \le \dfrac{1}{n}$ for all $n \ge 4$

     $\Longleftrightarrow 2^n \ge n^2$ for all $n \ge 4$

RESULT $\left\{n\left(\frac{1}{2}\right)^n\right\}$ is null, since $\left\{\frac{1}{n}\right\}$ is null.

$\boxed{\{n^p c^n\} \text{ is null, for } p > 0, \ |c| < 1}$

23. $\left\{\dfrac{10^n}{n!}\right\}$ is null

(clouds: $a_n = \dfrac{10^n}{n!}$, $b_n = ?$, $\lambda = ?$,   ✓ $\lambda = 30000$)

GUESS $\left\{\dfrac{10^n}{n!}\right\}$ is eventually dominated by $\left\{\dfrac{\lambda}{n}\right\}$

CHECK $\dfrac{10^n}{n!} = \underbrace{\left(\frac{10}{1}\right)\left(\frac{10}{2}\right)\cdots\left(\frac{10}{10}\right)}_{< 3000}\underbrace{\left(\frac{10}{11}\right)\cdots\left(\frac{10}{n-1}\right)}_{}\underbrace{\left(\frac{10}{n}\right)}_{\le 10/n}$

     so $\dfrac{10^n}{n!} < \dfrac{30000}{n}$ for all $n > 10$

RESULT $\left\{\dfrac{10^n}{n!}\right\}$ is null, since $\left\{\dfrac{30000}{n}\right\}$ is null.

$\boxed{\left\{\dfrac{c^n}{n!}\right\} \text{ is null, for } c \in \mathbb{R}}$

24. <u>Basic null sequences</u>

- $\left\{\dfrac{1}{n^p}\right\}$ for $p > 0$ Frame 9

- $\{c^n\}$ for $|c| < 1$ Frame 21

- $\{n^p c^n\}$ for $p > 0, \ |c| < 1$ Frame 22

- $\left\{\dfrac{c^n}{n!}\right\}$ for $c \in \mathbb{R}$ Frame 23

- $\left\{\dfrac{n^p}{n!}\right\}$ for $p > 0$ Subsection 2.2

2.2 Properties of null sequences

We now give a number of proofs which were omitted from the audio frames. First recall the definition of a *null* sequence.

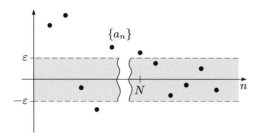

> **Definition**   The sequence $\{a_n\}$ is **null** if
>
> for each positive number ε, there is an integer N such that
>
> $$|a_n| < \varepsilon, \quad \text{for all } n > N. \tag{$*$}$$

Remarks

1. In statement $(*)$ we write 'for all $n > N$' to emphasise that the inequality $|a_n| < \varepsilon$ holds for every integer $n > N$. Note that statement $(*)$ can be rewritten as the implication

    if $n > N$, then $|a_n| < \varepsilon$.

2. The sequence $\{a_n\}$ is null if and only if the sequence $\{|a_n|\}$ is null.

    This is because statement $(*)$ is identical for the sequences $\{a_n\}$ and $\{|a_n|\}$. Similarly, $\{a_n\}$ is null if and only if $\{(-1)^n a_n\}$ is null.

3. The null sequence $\{a_n\}$ remains null if we add, delete or alter a finite number of terms to produce a new sequence $\{b_n\}$.

    This is because statement $(*)$ and its corresponding version for $\{b_n\}$ are identical, except that the values of N may differ by some integer.

    Informally, we say that 'finitely many terms do not matter'.

Proofs of the Power Rule and the Combination Rules

In the audio frames we proved the Squeeze Rule, but we did not prove the Power Rule and the Combination Rules. We now supply these proofs.

If you are short of time, omit these proofs.

> **Power Rule**   If $\{a_n\}$ is null, where $a_n \geq 0$, for $n = 1, 2, \ldots$, and if $p > 0$, then $\{a_n^p\}$ is null.

Proof   We want to prove that the sequence $\{a_n^p\}$ is null; that is:

for each positive number ε, there is an integer N such that

$$a_n^p < \varepsilon, \quad \text{for all } n > N. \tag{$*$}$$

We have $|a_n^p| = a_n^p$, since $a_n \geq 0$.

Let ε be a positive number. Since $\{a_n\}$ is null and $\varepsilon^{1/p}$ is positive, there is an integer N such that

$$a_n < \varepsilon^{1/p}, \quad \text{for all } n > N. \tag{$\dagger$}$$

Hence statement $(*)$ holds with this value of N. ∎

Remark   Note how we used $\varepsilon^{1/p}$ in statement (†) in order to obtain ε in statement (∗). We often prove the $\varepsilon - N$ statement (∗) for some new null sequence by applying the definition to a known null sequence (or sequences), using a positive number related in a suitable way to ε.

> **Sum Rule**   If $\{a_n\}$ and $\{b_n\}$ are null sequences, then $\{a_n + b_n\}$ is null.

Proof   We want to prove that the sequence $\{a_n + b_n\}$ is null; that is:

for each positive number ε, there is an integer N such that

$$|a_n + b_n| < \varepsilon, \quad \text{for all } n > N. \tag{∗}$$

Let ε be a positive number. Since $\{a_n\}$ and $\{b_n\}$ are null, there are integers N_1 and N_2 such that

$$|a_n| < \tfrac{1}{2}\varepsilon, \quad \text{for all } n > N_1,$$

and

$$|b_n| < \tfrac{1}{2}\varepsilon, \quad \text{for all } n > N_2.$$

We use $\tfrac{1}{2}\varepsilon$ here in order to obtain ε in statement (∗).

If $N = \max\{N_1, N_2\}$, then both the above inequalities hold for all $n > N$. Therefore, by the Triangle Inequality,

The Triangle Inequality was introduced in Unit AA1, Subsection 3.1.

$$|a_n + b_n| \leq |a_n| + |b_n| < \tfrac{1}{2}\varepsilon + \tfrac{1}{2}\varepsilon = \varepsilon, \quad \text{for all } n > N.$$

Thus statement (∗) holds with this value of N. ∎

> **Multiple Rule**   If $\{a_n\}$ is a null sequence, then $\{\lambda a_n\}$ is null, for $\lambda \in \mathbb{R}$.

Proof   We want to prove that the sequence $\{\lambda a_n\}$ is null; that is:

for each positive number ε, there is an integer N such that

$$|\lambda a_n| < \varepsilon, \quad \text{for all } n > N. \tag{∗}$$

If $\lambda = 0$, this statement is obvious, so we can assume that $\lambda \neq 0$.

Let ε be a positive number. Since $\{a_n\}$ is null, there is an integer N such that

$$|a_n| < \varepsilon/|\lambda|, \quad \text{for all } n > N;$$

We use $\varepsilon/|\lambda|$ here in order to obtain ε in statement (∗).

that is,

$$|\lambda a_n| < \varepsilon, \quad \text{for all } n > N.$$

Thus statement (∗) holds with this value of N. ∎

> **Product Rule**   If $\{a_n\}$ and $\{b_n\}$ are null sequences, then $\{a_n b_n\}$ is null.

Proof   We want to prove that the sequence $\{a_n b_n\}$ is null; that is:

for each positive number ε, there is an integer N such that

$$|a_n b_n| < \varepsilon, \quad \text{for all } n > N. \tag{$*$}$$

Let ε be a positive number. Since $\{a_n\}$ and $\{b_n\}$ are null, there are integers N_1 and N_2 such that

$$|a_n| < \sqrt{\varepsilon}, \quad \text{for all } n > N_1,$$

and

$$|b_n| < \sqrt{\varepsilon}, \quad \text{for all } n > N_2.$$

> We use $\sqrt{\varepsilon}$ here in order to obtain ε in statement $(*)$.

If $N = \max\{N_1, N_2\}$, then both the above inequalities hold for all $n > N$, so

$$|a_n b_n| = |a_n||b_n| < \sqrt{\varepsilon}\sqrt{\varepsilon} = \varepsilon, \quad \text{for all } n > N.$$

Thus statement $(*)$ holds with this value of N.   ∎

Basic null sequences

In the final audio frame we gave a list of basic null sequences. We end this section by proving that these sequences are null.

Basic null sequences   The following sequences are null.

(a) $\{1/n^p\}$, for $p > 0$.

(b) $\{c^n\}$, for $|c| < 1$.

(c) $\{n^p c^n\}$, for $p > 0, |c| < 1$.

(d) $\{c^n/n!\}$, for $c \in \mathbb{R}$.

(e) $\{n^p/n!\}$, for $p > 0$.

> For example:
>
> $\{1/n^{10}\}$;
>
> $\{(0.9)^n\}$;
>
> $\{n^3(\tfrac{1}{2})^n\} = \{n^3/2^n\}$;
>
> $\{10^n/n!\}$;
>
> $\{n^{10}/n!\}$.

Proof

(a) To prove that $\{1/n^p\}$ is null, for $p > 0$, we apply the Power Rule to the sequence $\{1/n\}$, which we know is null.

(b) To prove that $\{c^n\}$ is null, for $|c| < 1$, it is sufficient to consider only the case $0 \le c < 1$.

> If you are short of time, omit this proof.

> See remark 2 after the definition of a null sequence on page 18.

If $c = 0$, then the sequence is obviously null. Thus we can assume that $0 < c < 1$, so

$$c = \frac{1}{1+a}, \quad \text{where } a > 0.$$

By the Binomial Theorem,

> See Unit AA1, Subsection 3.3.

$$(1+a)^n \ge 1 + na \ge na, \quad \text{for } n = 1, 2, \ldots,$$

and hence

$$c^n = \frac{1}{(1+a)^n} \le \frac{1}{na}, \quad \text{for } n = 1, 2, \ldots.$$

Since $\{1/n\}$ is null, we deduce that $\{1/(na)\}$ is null, by the Multiple Rule. Hence $\{c^n\}$ is null, by the Squeeze Rule, as required.

(c) To prove that $\{n^p c^n\}$ is null, for $p > 0$ and $|c| < 1$, we can again assume that $0 < c < 1$, so

$$c = \frac{1}{1+a}, \quad \text{where } a > 0.$$

First we deal with the case $p = 1$. By the Binomial Theorem,

$$(1 + a)^n \geq 1 + na + \tfrac{1}{2}n(n - 1)a^2 \geq \tfrac{1}{2}n(n - 1)a^2, \quad \text{for } n = 2, 3, \ldots,$$

so

$$nc^n = \frac{n}{(1 + a)^n} \leq \frac{n}{\tfrac{1}{2}n(n - 1)a^2} = \frac{(2/a^2)}{n - 1}, \quad \text{for } n = 2, 3, \ldots.$$

Now $\{(2/a^2)/(n - 1)\}_2^\infty$ is null by the Multiple Rule. Hence $\{nc^n\}$ is null, by the Squeeze Rule. This proves part (c) in the case $p = 1$.

To deduce that $\{n^p c^n\}$ is null for any $p > 0$ and $0 < c < 1$, we note that

$$n^p c^n = (nd^n)^p, \quad \text{for } n = 1, 2, \ldots,$$

where $d = c^{1/p}$. Since $0 < d < 1$, we know that $\{nd^n\}$ is null, so $\{n^p c^n\}$ is null, by the Power Rule.

Here we use the fact that

$$\left\{ \frac{1}{n - 1} \right\}_2^\infty \quad \text{and} \quad \left\{ \frac{1}{n} \right\}_1^\infty$$

are the same sequence, since they have the same terms:

$$1, \tfrac{1}{2}, \tfrac{1}{3}, \ldots.$$

(d) To prove that $\{c^n/n!\}$ is null, we can assume that $c > 0$. We first choose an integer m such that $m + 1 > c$. Then, for $n > m + 1$,

$$\frac{c^n}{n!} = \left(\frac{c}{1} \right) \left(\frac{c}{2} \right) \cdots \left(\frac{c}{m} \right) \left(\frac{c}{m + 1} \right) \cdots \left(\frac{c}{n - 1} \right) \left(\frac{c}{n} \right)$$

$$\leq \left(\frac{c}{1} \right) \left(\frac{c}{2} \right) \cdots \left(\frac{c}{m} \right) \times \frac{c}{n}$$

$$= K \times \frac{c}{n},$$

where $K = c^m/m!$ is a constant.

Since $\{1/n\}$ is null, we deduce that $\{Kc/n\}$ is null, by the Multiple Rule. Hence $\{c^n/n!\}$ is null, by the Squeeze Rule.

(e) To prove that $\{n^p/n!\}$ is null for $p > 0$, we write

$$\frac{n^p}{n!} = \left(\frac{n^p}{2^n} \right) \left(\frac{2^n}{n!} \right), \quad \text{for } n = 1, 2, \ldots.$$

Since $\{n^p/2^n\}$ and $\{2^n/n!\}$ are both null sequences, by parts (c) and (d), we deduce that $\{n^p/n!\}$ is null, by the Product Rule. ∎

Further exercises

Exercise 2.6 For each of the following sequences $\{a_n\}$ and positive numbers ε, find an integer N such that

$$|a_n| < \varepsilon, \quad \text{for all } n > N.$$

(a) $a_n = (-1)^n/n^5, \quad \varepsilon = 0.001.$ (b) $a_n = 1/(2n + 1)^2, \quad \varepsilon = 0.002.$

Exercise 2.7 Use the definition of null sequence to prove that the two sequences in Exercise 2.6 are null.

Exercise 2.8 Prove that the following sequences are not null.

(a) $\{\sqrt{n}\}$ (b) $\{1 + (-1)^n/n\}$

Exercise 2.9 Use the fact that $\{1/n\}$ is null to deduce that the following sequences are null. State which rules you use.

(a) $\left\{ \dfrac{2}{\sqrt{n}} + \dfrac{3}{n^7} \right\}$ (b) $\left\{ \dfrac{\cos n}{n^2 + 1} \right\}$ (c) $\left\{ \dfrac{n!}{n^n} \right\}$

Exercise 2.10 Use the identity $a - b = (a^2 - b^2)/(a + b)$ to prove that the sequence $\{\sqrt{n + 1} - \sqrt{n}\}$ is null.

Exercise 2.11   Use the list of basic null sequences (Frame 24) to prove that the following sequences are null. State which rules you use.

(a) $\left\{ \dfrac{3}{4^n} + \dfrac{2n}{3^n} \right\}$ (b) $\left\{ \dfrac{6n^{10}}{n!} \right\}$ (c) $\left\{ \dfrac{n^{10}10^n}{n!} \right\}$

In part (c), you can express the sequence as a product of basic null sequences.

3   Convergent sequences

After working through this section, you should be able to:

(a) explain what is meant by the statement $\lim\limits_{n\to\infty} a_n = l$, or $a_n \to l$ as $n \to \infty$;

(b) use the Combination Rules to calculate limits of sequences;

(c) state and use some theorems about convergent sequences.

3.1 What is a convergent sequence?

In the previous section we looked at null sequences, that is, sequences which converge to 0. We turn our attention now to sequences which converge to limits other than 0.

Exercise 3.1   Consider the sequence

$$a_n = \frac{n+1}{n}, \quad n = 1, 2, \ldots.$$

(a) Draw the sequence diagram of $\{a_n\}$ and describe (informally) how this sequence behaves.

(b) What can you say (formally) about the behaviour of the sequence

$$b_n = a_n - 1, \quad n = 1, 2, \ldots?$$

The terms of the sequence $\{a_n\}$ in Exercise 3.1 appear to approach arbitrarily close to 1; that is, the sequence $\{a_n\}$ appears to converge to 1. If we subtract 1 from each term a_n to form the sequence $\{b_n\}$, then we obtain a null sequence. This example suggests the following definition of a *convergent sequence*.

Definition   The sequence $\{a_n\}$ is **convergent** with **limit** l if $\{a_n - l\}$ is a null sequence. We say that $\{a_n\}$ **converges to** l and we write

EITHER $\lim\limits_{n\to\infty} a_n = l$

OR $a_n \to l$ as $n \to \infty$.

These statements are read as:

'the limit of a_n, as n tends to infinity, is l';

'a_n tends to l, as n tends to infinity'.

Often we omit 'as $n \to \infty$'.

Do not let this use of the *symbol* ∞ tempt you to think that ∞ is a real number.

The following are examples of convergent sequences:

every null sequence converges to 0;

every constant sequence $\{c\}$ converges to c;

the sequence $\{(n+1)/n\}$ is convergent and

$$\lim_{n\to\infty} \left(\frac{n+1}{n} \right) = 1.$$

See Exercise 3.1.

Exercise 3.2   Show that the sequence

$$a_n = \frac{n^3 + 1}{2n^3}, \quad n = 1, 2, \ldots,$$

converges to $\frac{1}{2}$, by considering $a_n - \frac{1}{2}$.

The definition of convergence of a sequence is often given in the following equivalent (alternative) form.

Definition (alternative)   The sequence $\{a_n\}$ **converges to** l if

for each positive number ε, there is an integer N such that

$|a_n - l| < \varepsilon, \quad$ for all $n > N$.

Remarks

1. In terms of the sequence diagram for $\{a_n\}$, this definition states that:

    for each positive number ε, the terms a_n *eventually* lie inside the horizontal strip from $l - \varepsilon$ to $l + \varepsilon$.

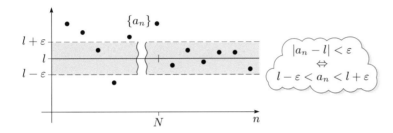

2. If a sequence is convergent, then it has a unique limit. A proof of this seemingly obvious fact is given later in this section as a corollary to the Limit Inequality Rule.

3. If a given sequence converges to l, then this remains true if we add, delete or alter a finite number of terms. This follows from the corresponding result for null sequences.

    See Subsection 2.2.

4. Not all sequences are convergent. For example, the sequence $\{(-1)^n\}$ is not convergent.

    We discuss non-convergent sequences in Section 4.

3.2 Combination Rules for convergent sequences

So far you have tested the convergence of a given sequence $\{a_n\}$ by calculating $a_n - l$ and showing that $\{a_n - l\}$ is null. This presupposes that you know in advance the value of l. Usually, however, you are given a sequence $\{a_n\}$ and asked to decide whether or not it converges and, if it does, to *find* its limit. Fortunately, the convergence of many sequences can be proved by using the following Combination Rules, which extend the Combination Rules for null sequences.

See Subsection 2.1, Frame 10.

Combination Rules   If $\lim\limits_{n\to\infty} a_n = l$ and $\lim\limits_{n\to\infty} b_n = m$, then

Sum Rule $\lim\limits_{n\to\infty} (a_n + b_n) = l + m$;

Multiple Rule $\lim\limits_{n\to\infty} (\lambda a_n) = \lambda l$, for $\lambda \in \mathbb{R}$;

Product Rule $\lim\limits_{n\to\infty} (a_n b_n) = lm$;

Quotient Rule $\lim\limits_{n\to\infty} \left(\dfrac{a_n}{b_n} \right) = \dfrac{l}{m}$, provided that $m \neq 0$.

Remark   In applications of the Quotient Rule, some terms b_n can take the value 0, in which case a_n/b_n is not defined. However, we shall see (in Lemma 3.1) that because $m \neq 0$ this occurs for only *finitely many* b_n, so $\{b_n\}$ is eventually non-zero. Thus the statement of the Quotient Rule does make sense.

We prove the Combination Rules at the end of this subsection, but first we illustrate how to apply them.

Applying the Combination Rules

Example 3.1   Show that each of the following sequences $\{a_n\}$ is convergent and find its limit.

(a) $a_n = \dfrac{(2n + 1)(n + 2)}{3n^2 + 3n}$ (b) $a_n = \dfrac{2n^2 + 10^n}{n! + 3n^3}$

Solution   Although the expressions for a_n are quotients, we cannot apply the Quotient Rule immediately because the sequences defined by the numerators and the denominators are not convergent. In each case, however, we can rearrange the expressions for a_n and then apply the Combination Rules.

(a) We divide both the numerator and the denominator by n^2 to give

$$a_n = \frac{(2n + 1)(n + 2)}{3n^2 + 3n} = \frac{(2 + 1/n)(1 + 2/n)}{3 + 3/n}.$$

Since $\{1/n\}$ is a basic null sequence, we find, by the Combination Rules, that

$$\lim_{n\to\infty} a_n = \frac{(2 + 0)(1 + 0)}{3 + 0} = \frac{2}{3}.$$

The basic null sequences are:

$$\left\{ \frac{1}{n^p} \right\}, \text{for } p > 0;$$

$$\{c^n\}, \text{for } |c| < 1;$$

$$\{n^p c^n\}, \text{for } p > 0, |c| < 1;$$

$$\left\{ \frac{c^n}{n!} \right\}, \text{for } c \in \mathbb{R};$$

$$\left\{ \frac{n^p}{n!} \right\}, \text{for } p > 0.$$

(b) We divide both the numerator and the denominator by $n!$ to give

$$a_n = \frac{2n^2 + 10^n}{n! + 3n^3} = \frac{2n^2/n! + 10^n/n!}{1 + 3n^3/n!}.$$

Since $\{n^2/n!\}$, $\{10^n/n!\}$ and $\{n^3/n!\}$ are all basic null sequences, we find, by the Combination Rules, that

$$\lim_{n\to\infty} a_n = \frac{0 + 0}{1 + 0} = 0. \quad \blacksquare$$

We simplified each of the above examples by dividing both the numerator and denominator by the *dominant term*, which was chosen in such a way that the resulting quotients in the numerator and denominator are all terms of convergent sequences.

In part (a) we divided by n^2, which is the highest power of n in the expression.

In part (b) we divided by $n!$ because $\{n^2/n!\}, \{10^n/n!\}, \{1\}$ and $\{n^3/n!\}$ are all convergent sequences.

These examples illustrate the following general strategy.

Strategy 3.1   To evaluate the limit of a complicated quotient.

1. Identify the dominant term.

2. Divide both numerator and denominator by the dominant term.

3. Apply the Combination Rules.

Note that

$$n! \text{ dominates } c^n,$$

and, for $|c| > 1$ and $p > 0$,

$$c^n \text{ dominates } n^p.$$

Exercise 3.3   Show that each of the following sequences $\{a_n\}$ is convergent and find its limit.

(a) $a_n = \dfrac{n^3 + 2n^2 + 3}{2n^3 + 1}$ (b) $a_n = \dfrac{n^2 + 2^n}{3^n + n^3}$ (c) $a_n = \dfrac{n! + (-1)^n}{2^n + 3n!}$

Hint: In Exercise 3.3(b) you can use the fact that $\{2^n/3^n\}$ is a basic null sequence because $2^n/3^n = (2/3)^n$, for $n = 1, 2, \ldots$.

Proofs of the Combination Rules

We prove the Sum Rule, the Multiple Rule and the Product Rule by using the corresponding Combination Rules for null sequences. Remember that

$$\lim_{n \to \infty} a_n = l \quad \text{means that} \quad \{a_n - l\} \text{ is a null sequence.}$$

If you are short of time, omit these proofs.

Sum Rule   If $\lim\limits_{n \to \infty} a_n = l$ and $\lim\limits_{n \to \infty} b_n = m$, then

$$\lim_{n \to \infty} (a_n + b_n) = l + m.$$

Proof   We know that $\{a_n - l\}$ and $\{b_n - m\}$ are null sequences. Since

$$(a_n + b_n) - (l + m) = (a_n - l) + (b_n - m),$$

we deduce that $\{(a_n + b_n) - (l + m)\}$ is null, by the Sum Rule for null sequences.   ∎

Product Rule   If $\lim\limits_{n \to \infty} a_n = l$ and $\lim\limits_{n \to \infty} b_n = m$, then

$$\lim_{n \to \infty} (a_n b_n) = lm.$$

The Multiple Rule is a special case of the Product Rule in which the sequence $\{b_n\}$ is a constant sequence.

Proof   Here we express $a_n b_n - lm$ in terms of $a_n - l$ and $b_n - m$:

$$a_n b_n - lm = (a_n - l)(b_n - m) + m(a_n - l) + l(b_n - m).$$

Since $\{a_n - l\}$ and $\{b_n - m\}$ are null, we deduce that $\{a_n b_n - lm\}$ is null, by the Combination Rules for null sequences.   ∎

To prove the Quotient Rule we use the following lemma, which shows that if the limit of a sequence is positive, then the terms of the sequence must be eventually positive.

> **Lemma 3.1**   If $\lim\limits_{n \to \infty} a_n = l$ and $l > 0$, then there is an integer N such that
>
> $$a_n > \tfrac{1}{2}l, \quad \text{for all } n > N.$$

Proof   Since $\tfrac{1}{2}l > 0$, there is an integer N such that

$$|a_n - l| < \tfrac{1}{2}l, \quad \text{for all } n > N.$$

Take $\varepsilon = \tfrac{1}{2}l$ in the alternative definition of convergence.

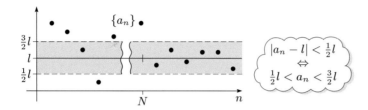

Hence

$$-\tfrac{1}{2}l < a_n - l < \tfrac{1}{2}l, \quad \text{for all } n > N,$$

and the left-hand inequality gives

$$\tfrac{1}{2}l < a_n, \quad \text{for all } n > N,$$

as required.   ■

> **Quotient Rule**   If $\lim\limits_{n \to \infty} a_n = l$ and $\lim\limits_{n \to \infty} b_n = m$, then
>
> $$\lim_{n \to \infty} \left(\frac{a_n}{b_n} \right) = \frac{l}{m}, \quad \text{provided that } m \neq 0.$$

Proof   We assume that $m > 0$; the proof for the case $m < 0$ is similar. Once again the idea is to write the required expression in terms of $a_n - l$ and $b_n - m$:

$$\frac{a_n}{b_n} - \frac{l}{m} = \frac{m(a_n - l) - l(b_n - m)}{b_n m}.$$

Now, however, there is a slight problem: $\{m(a_n - l) - l(b_n - m)\}$ is certainly a null sequence, but the denominator is rather awkward. Some of the terms b_n can take the value 0, in which case the expression is undefined.

However, by Lemma 3.1, we know that for some integer N we have

$$b_n > \tfrac{1}{2}m, \quad \text{for all } n > N.$$

This statement implies that the terms of $\{b_n\}$ are eventually positive.

Thus, for all $n > N$,

$$
\begin{aligned}
\left| \frac{a_n}{b_n} - \frac{l}{m} \right| &= \frac{|m(a_n - l) - l(b_n - m)|}{b_n m} \\
&\leq \frac{|m(a_n - l) - l(b_n - m)|}{\tfrac{1}{2}m^2}.
\end{aligned}
$$

Since the right-hand side defines a null sequence, it follows, by the Squeeze Rule for null sequences, that $\left\{ \dfrac{a_n}{b_n} - \dfrac{l}{m} \right\}$ is null, as required.   ■

3.3 Further rules for convergent sequences

There are several other theorems about convergent sequences, which are needed in later units. The first is a general version of the Squeeze Rule.

Squeeze Rule If $\{a_n\}$, $\{b_n\}$ and $\{c_n\}$ are sequences such that

1. $b_n \leq a_n \leq c_n$, for $n = 1, 2, \ldots,$
2. $\displaystyle\lim_{n\to\infty} b_n = \lim_{n\to\infty} c_n = l,$

then $\displaystyle\lim_{n\to\infty} a_n = l.$

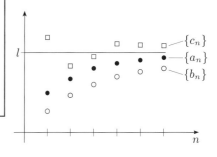

Proof By the Combination Rules,

$$\lim_{n\to\infty} (c_n - b_n) = l - l = 0,$$

so $\{c_n - b_n\}$ is a null sequence. Also, by condition 1,

$$0 \leq a_n - b_n \leq c_n - b_n, \quad \text{for } n = 1, 2, \ldots,$$

so $\{a_n - b_n\}$ is null, by the Squeeze Rule for null sequences.

Now we write a_n in the form

$$a_n = (a_n - b_n) + b_n.$$

Hence, by the Combination Rules,

$$\lim_{n\to\infty} a_n = \lim_{n\to\infty} (a_n - b_n) + \lim_{n\to\infty} b_n = 0 + l = l. \quad \blacksquare$$

Remark In applications of the Squeeze Rule, it is sufficient to check that condition 1 holds *eventually*. This is because the values of a *finite* number of terms do not affect convergence.

Finitely many terms do not matter.

The following example and exercise illustrate the use of the Squeeze Rule and the Binomial Theorem in the derivation of two important limits.

Example 3.2

(a) Prove that if $c > 0$, then

$$(1 + c)^{1/n} \leq 1 + \frac{c}{n}, \quad \text{for } n = 1, 2, \ldots.$$

We proved this inequality for the case $c = 1$ in Unit AA1, Section 3, Frame 5.

(b) Use the Squeeze Rule to deduce that if $a > 0$, then

$$\lim_{n\to\infty} a^{1/n} = 1.$$

Solution

(a) Using the rules for equivalent inequalities, we obtain

$$(1 + c)^{1/n} \leq 1 + \frac{c}{n} \Leftrightarrow 1 + c \leq \left(1 + \frac{c}{n}\right)^n.$$

See Unit AA1, Section 2, Rule 5 with $p = n$.

The right-hand inequality holds because

$$\left(1 + \frac{c}{n}\right)^n \geq 1 + n\left(\frac{c}{n}\right) = 1 + c,$$

by the Binomial Theorem, so the left-hand inequality also holds.

(b) We consider the cases $a > 1$, $a = 1$ and $0 < a < 1$ separately.

If $a > 1$, then we can write $a = 1 + c$, where $c > 0$.

By part (a),

$$1 \leq a^{1/n} = (1+c)^{1/n} \leq 1 + \frac{c}{n}, \quad \text{for } n = 1, 2, \ldots.$$

Since $\lim_{n \to \infty} \left(1 + \frac{c}{n}\right) = 1$, we deduce, by the Squeeze Rule, that

$$\lim_{n \to \infty} a^{1/n} = 1.$$

In this application of the Squeeze Rule, the 'lower' sequence is $\{1\}$.

If $a = 1$, then $a^{1/n} = 1$, for $n = 1, 2, \ldots$, so

$$\lim_{n \to \infty} a^{1/n} = 1.$$

If $0 < a < 1$, then $1/a > 1$, so $\lim_{n \to \infty} (1/a)^{1/n} = 1$, by the first case. Hence, by the Quotient Rule,

$$\lim_{n \to \infty} a^{1/n} = \frac{1}{\lim_{n \to \infty} (1/a)^{1/n}} = \frac{1}{1} = 1. \quad \blacksquare$$

Exercise 3.4

(a) Prove that

$$n^{1/n} \leq 1 + \sqrt{\frac{2}{n-1}}, \quad \text{for } n \geq 2.$$

Hint: By the Binomial Theorem, we have

$$(1+x)^n \geq \frac{n(n-1)}{2!} x^2, \quad \text{for } n \geq 2, \ x \geq 0.$$

(b) Use the Squeeze Rule to deduce from part (a) that

$$\lim_{n \to \infty} n^{1/n} = 1.$$

Next we show that taking limits preserves weak inequalities.

Limit Inequality Rule   If $\lim_{n \to \infty} a_n = l$ and $\lim_{n \to \infty} b_n = m$, and also

$$a_n \leq b_n, \quad \text{for } n = 1, 2, \ldots,$$

then $l \leq m$.

Proof   Suppose that $a_n \to l$, $b_n \to m$ and $a_n \leq b_n$, for $n = 1, 2, \ldots$. If $l > m$, then, by the Combination Rules,

$$\lim_{n \to \infty} (a_n - b_n) = l - m > 0.$$

This is a proof by contradiction.

Hence, by Lemma 3.1, there is an integer N such that

$$a_n - b_n > \tfrac{1}{2}(l - m), \quad \text{for all } n > N. \tag{3.1}$$

Since $a_n - b_n \leq 0$, for $n = 1, 2, \ldots$, statement (3.1) gives a contradiction.

Hence the inequality $l \leq m$ is true. $\blacksquare$

We can now give the proof, promised earlier, that a convergent sequence has a unique limit.

See page 23.

Corollary If $\lim_{n \to \infty} a_n = l$ and $\lim_{n \to \infty} a_n = m$, then $l = m$.

Proof Applying the Limit Inequality Rule with $b_n = a_n$, we deduce that $l \le m$ and also that $m \le l$. Hence $l = m$. ∎

Remark Taking limits does not preserve *strict* inequalities. For example, if $a_n = 1/n$, $n = 1, 2, \ldots$, and $b_n = 2/n$, $n = 1, 2, \ldots$, then

$$a_n < b_n, \quad \text{for } n = 1, 2, \ldots .$$

But it is not true that $\lim_{n \to \infty} a_n < \lim_{n \to \infty} b_n$, since both limits are 0.

In Section 2, we pointed out that a sequence $\{a_n\}$ is null if and only if the sequence $\{|a_n|\}$ is null. The final theorem in this section is a partial generalisation of this result.

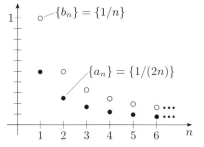

Theorem 3.1 If $\lim_{n \to \infty} a_n = l$, then $\lim_{n \to \infty} |a_n| = |l|$.

Proof Using the backwards form of the Triangle Inequality, we obtain

$$\big| |a_n| - |l| \big| \le |a_n - l|, \quad \text{for } n = 1, 2, \ldots .$$

Since $\{a_n - l\}$ is null, we deduce from the Squeeze Rule for null sequences that $\{|a_n| - |l|\}$ is null, as required. ∎

See Unit AA1, Subsection 3.1.

Remark Theorem 3.1 is only a partial generalisation of the earlier result about null sequences because the converse statement is false. If $|a_n| \to |l|$, then it does *not* follow that $a_n \to l$. For example, consider the sequence $a_n = (-1)^n$, $n = 1, 2, \ldots$; in this case,

$$|a_n| \to 1 \text{ as } n \to \infty,$$

but $\{a_n\}$ does not converge.

Further exercises

Exercise 3.5 Show that the following sequences converge to 1, by calculating $a_n - 1$ in each case.

(a) $\left\{ \dfrac{n-1}{n+3} \right\}$ (b) $\left\{ \dfrac{n^2}{n^2 + n + 1} \right\}$

Exercise 3.6 Use the Combination Rules to find the limits of the following sequences.

(a) $\left\{ \dfrac{n^2}{n^2 + n + 1} \right\}$ (b) $\left\{ \dfrac{n^2 - 2^n}{2^n + n^{20}} \right\}$ (c) $\left\{ \dfrac{5n! + 5^n}{n^{100} + n!} \right\}$

Exercise 3.7 Prove that if $\{a_n\}$ is convergent with limit l, then $\{a_n^2\}$ is convergent with limit l^2.

4   Divergent sequences

After working through this section, you should be able to:

(a) explain the terms *divergent* sequence, *bounded* sequence and *unbounded* sequence;

(b) explain the phrases $\{a_n\}$ *tends to infinity* and $\{a_n\}$ *tends to minus infinity*, and use the Reciprocal Rule to recognise sequences which tend to infinity;

(c) use the subsequence rules to recognise divergent sequences.

4.1   What is a divergent sequence?

We have commented several times that not all sequences are convergent. We now investigate the behaviour of sequences which do not converge.

> **Definition**   A sequence is **divergent** if it is not convergent.

Here are the sequence diagrams for $\{(-1)^n\}$, $\{2n\}$ and $\{(-1)^n n\}$. Each of these sequences is divergent but, as you can see, they behave differently.

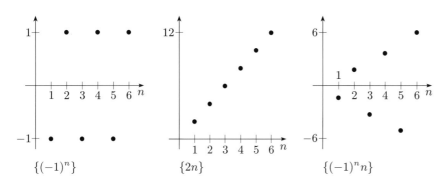

$\{(-1)^n\}$ $\{2n\}$ $\{(-1)^n n\}$

It is not easy to prove from the definition that these sequences are divergent.

In this section we obtain criteria for divergence which avoid us having to argue directly from the definition. At the end of the section we give a strategy for divergence involving two criteria, which together cover all cases. We obtain these criteria by establishing certain properties which are necessarily possessed by a convergent sequence; if a sequence does not have one of these properties, then it must be divergent.

For example, to show that the sequence $\{(-1)^n\}$ is divergent, we have to show that $\{(-1)^n\}$ is not convergent; that is, for every real number l, the sequence $\{(-1)^n - l\}$ is not null.

4.2   Bounded and unbounded sequences

One property possessed by a convergent sequence is that it must be *bounded*.

> **Definition**   A sequence $\{a_n\}$ is **bounded** if there is a number K such that
>
> $$|a_n| \leq K, \quad \text{for } n = 1, 2, \ldots.$$
>
> A sequence is **unbounded** if it is not bounded.

Thus a sequence $\{a_n\}$ is bounded if *all* the terms a_n lie on the sequence diagram in the horizontal strip from $-K$ to K, for some positive number K.

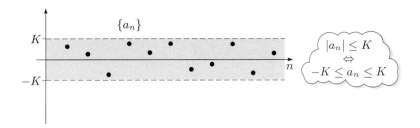

For example, the sequence $\{(-1)^n\}$ is bounded because

$$|(-1)^n| \leq 1, \quad \text{for } n = 1, 2, \ldots.$$

However, the sequences $\{2n\}$ and $\{n^2\}$ are unbounded, since, for each positive number K, we can find terms of these sequences whose absolute values are greater than K.

> **Exercise 4.1**   Classify the following sequences as bounded or unbounded.
>
> (a) $\{1 + (-1)^n\}$ (b) $\{(-1)^n n\}$ (c) $\left\{ \dfrac{2n + 1}{n} \right\}$

The sequence $\{(-1)^n\}$ shows that

   a bounded sequence is not necessarily convergent.

However, we can prove that

   a convergent sequence is necessarily bounded.

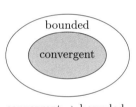

convergent $\Rightarrow$ bounded

Theorem 4.1   If $\{a_n\}$ is convergent, then $\{a_n\}$ is bounded.

Proof   We know that $a_n \to l$, for some real number l. Thus $\{a_n - l\}$ is a null sequence, so there is an integer N such that

$$|a_n - l| < 1, \quad \text{for all } n > N.$$

Now

$$
\begin{aligned}
|a_n| &= |(a_n - l) + l| \\
&\leq |a_n - l| + |l|, \quad \text{by the Triangle Inequality.}
\end{aligned}
$$

Take $\varepsilon = 1$ in the definition of a null sequence on page 18.

It follows that

$$|a_n| < 1 + |l|, \quad \text{for all } n > N.$$

This is the type of inequality needed to prove that $\{a_n\}$ is bounded, but it does not include the terms $a_1, a_2, \ldots, a_N$. To complete the proof, we put

$$K = |a_1| + |a_2| + \cdots + |a_N| + 1 + |l|.$$

It then follows that

$$|a_n| \leq K, \quad \text{for } n = 1, 2, \ldots,$$

as required.   ∎

From Theorem 4.1, we obtain the following test for the *divergence* of a sequence.

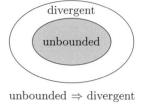

divergent

unbounded

unbounded ⇒ divergent

> **Corollary** If $\{a_n\}$ is unbounded, then $\{a_n\}$ is divergent.

For example, the sequences $\{2n\}$ and $\{(-1)^n n\}$ are both unbounded, so they are both divergent, by the corollary to Theorem 4.1.

> **Exercise 4.2** Classify the following sequences as bounded or unbounded and as convergent or divergent.
>
> (a) $\{\sqrt{n}\}$ (b) $\left\{\dfrac{n^2 + n}{n^2 + 1}\right\}$ (c) $\{(-1)^n n^2\}$ (d) $\{n^{(-1)^n}\}$

4.3 Sequences tending to infinity

Although the sequences $\{2n\}$ and $\{(-1)^n n\}$ are both unbounded and hence divergent, there is a marked difference in their behaviour. Informally, the terms of both sequences become arbitrarily large, but those of the sequence $\{2n\}$ become arbitrarily large and positive. The following definition makes this informal idea precise.

> **Definition** The sequence $\{a_n\}$ **tends to infinity** if
>
> for each positive number K, there is an integer N such that
>
> $a_n > K, \quad$ for all $n > N$.
>
> In this case, we write
>
> $a_n \to \infty \;$ as $n \to \infty$.

Often, we omit 'as $n \to \infty$'.

Remarks

1. In terms of the sequence diagram for $\{a_n\}$, this definition states that, for each positive number K, the terms a_n eventually lie above the horizontal line at height K.

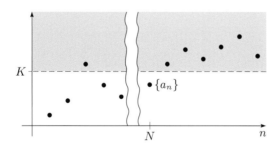

2. In this course we do not use the $\lim\limits_{n \to \infty}$ notation for sequences that tend to infinity because the symbol ∞ is not a limit.

3. If a sequence tends to infinity, then it is unbounded and hence divergent, by the corollary to Theorem 4.1.

4. If a given sequence tends to infinity, then this remains true if we add, delete or alter a finite number of terms.

Finitely many terms do not matter.

The next rule enables us to use our knowledge of null sequences to identify sequences which tend to infinity.

Reciprocal Rule   If the sequence $\{a_n\}$ satisfies both the conditions

1. $\{a_n\}$ is eventually positive,

2. $\{1/a_n\}$ is a null sequence,

then $a_n \to \infty$.

There is a converse to this rule, which states that if $a_n \to \infty$, then $1/a_n \to 0$.

Proof   To prove that $a_n \to \infty$, we have to show that:

for each positive number K, there is an integer N such that

$$a_n > K, \quad \text{for all } n > N. \qquad (*)$$

Let K be a positive number. Since $\{a_n\}$ is eventually positive, we can choose an integer N_1 such that

$$a_n > 0, \quad \text{for all } n > N_1.$$

Since $\{1/a_n\}$ is null, we can choose an integer N_2 such that

$$\left| \frac{1}{a_n} \right| < \frac{1}{K}, \quad \text{for all } n > N_2.$$

Take $\varepsilon = 1/K$ in the definition of a null sequence.

Let $N = \max\{N_1, N_2\}$; then

$$0 < \frac{1}{a_n} < \frac{1}{K}, \quad \text{for all } n > N.$$

This statement is equivalent to statement $(*)$, so $a_n \to \infty$.   ■

Example 4.1   Use the Reciprocal Rule to prove that the following sequences tend to infinity.

(a) $\{n^3/2\}$ (b) $\{n! + 10^n\}$ (c) $\{n! - 10^n\}$

In parts (b) and (c), $n!$ is the dominant term.

Solution

(a) Each term of the sequence $\{n^3/2\}$ is positive and $(n^3/2)^{-1} = 2/n^3$. Now, $\{1/n^3\}$ is a basic null sequence, so $\{2/n^3\}$ is null, by the Multiple Rule.

   Hence $n^3/2 \to \infty$, by the Reciprocal Rule.

(b) Each term of the sequence $\{n! + 10^n\}$ is positive.

   The dominant term is $n!$, so we write

   $$\frac{1}{n! + 10^n} = \frac{1/n!}{1 + 10^n/n!}.$$

   Now, $\{1/n!\}$ and $\{10^n/n!\}$ are basic null sequences. Thus, by the Combination Rules,

   $$\lim_{n \to \infty} \frac{1}{n! + 10^n} = \lim_{n \to \infty} \frac{1/n!}{1 + 10^n/n!} = \frac{0}{1 + 0} = 0.$$

   Hence $n! + 10^n \to \infty$, by the Reciprocal Rule.

Alternatively, since
$$\frac{1}{n! + 10^n} \le \frac{1}{n!},$$
the sequence $\left\{ \dfrac{1}{n! + 10^n} \right\}$ is null, by the Squeeze Rule for null sequences.

(c) The dominant term is $n!$, so we first write

   $$n! - 10^n = n!(1 - 10^n/n!), \quad \text{for } n = 1, 2, \dots .$$

   Since $\{10^n/n!\}$ is a basic null sequence, we know that $10^n/n!$ is eventually less than 1, so $\{n! - 10^n\}$ is eventually positive.

   Next we write

   $$\frac{1}{n! - 10^n} = \frac{1/n!}{1 - 10^n/n!}.$$

Now, $\{1/n!\}$ and $\{10^n/n!\}$ are basic null sequences. Thus, by the Combination Rules,

$$\lim_{n\to\infty} \frac{1}{n! - 10^n} = \lim_{n\to\infty} \frac{1/n!}{1 - 10^n/n!} = \frac{0}{1-0} = 0.$$

Hence $n! - 10^n \to \infty$, by the Reciprocal Rule. ∎

There are also versions of the Combination Rules and Squeeze Rule for sequences which tend to infinity. We state these without proof.

Combination Rules   If $\{a_n\}$ tends to infinity and $\{b_n\}$ tends to infinity, then

Sum Rule $\{a_n + b_n\}$ tends to infinity;

Multiple Rule $\{\lambda a_n\}$ tends to infinity, for $\lambda \in \mathbb{R}^+$;

Product Rule $\{a_n b_n\}$ tends to infinity.

Recall that
$$\mathbb{R}^+ = \{x : x > 0\}.$$

Squeeze Rule   If $\{b_n\}$ tends to infinity and

$$a_n \geq b_n, \quad \text{for } n = 1, 2, \ldots,$$

then $\{a_n\}$ tends to infinity.

Exercise 4.3   For each of the following sequences $\{a_n\}$, prove that $a_n \to \infty$.

(a) $\{2^n/n\}$

(b) $\{2^n - n^9\}$

(c) $\{2^n/n + 5n^9\}$

(d) $\left\{ \dfrac{2^n + n^2}{n^9 + n} \right\}$

We can also define $\{a_n\}$ *tends to minus infinity*.

Definition   The sequence $\{a_n\}$ **tends to minus infinity** if

$$-a_n \to \infty \quad \text{as } n \to \infty.$$

We write

$$a_n \to -\infty \quad \text{as } n \to \infty.$$

Some texts use the symbol $+\infty$ rather than ∞ in order to have symmetry with the symbol $-\infty$.

For example, the sequences $\{-n^2\}$ and $\{10^n - n!\}$ both tend to minus infinity because $\{n^2\}$ and $\{n! - 10^n\}$ tend to infinity. Sequences which tend to minus infinity are unbounded and hence divergent. However, the sequence $\{(-1)^n n\}$ shows that an unbounded sequence need not tend to infinity nor to minus infinity.

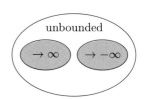

4.4 Subsequences

In this subsection we give two useful criteria for establishing that a sequence diverges; both of them involve the idea of a *subsequence*. For example, consider the bounded divergent sequence $\{(-1)^n\}$. This sequence splits naturally into two:

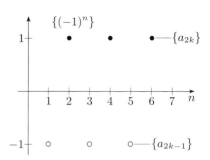

the *even* terms $a_2, a_4, \ldots, a_{2k}, \ldots$, each of which equals 1;

the *odd* terms $a_1, a_3, \ldots, a_{2k-1}, \ldots$, each of which equals -1.

Both these are sequences in their own right, and we call them the **even subsequence** $\{a_{2k}\}$ and the **odd subsequence** $\{a_{2k-1}\}$.

In general, given a sequence $\{a_n\}$, we can consider many different subsequences, such as:

$\{a_{3k}\}$, comprising the terms $a_3, a_6, a_9, \ldots$;

$\{a_{4k+1}\}$, comprising the terms $a_5, a_9, a_{13}, \ldots$;

$\{a_{k!}\}$, comprising the terms $a_1, a_2, a_6, \ldots$.

Definition   The sequence $\{a_{n_k}\}$ is a **subsequence** of the sequence $\{a_n\}$ if $\{n_k\}$ is a strictly increasing sequence of positive integers; that is,

$$n_1 < n_2 < n_3 < \cdots.$$

The sequence $\{a_{n_k}\}$ has terms
$$a_{n_1}, a_{n_2}, a_{n_3}, \cdots.$$
As a special case, the sequence $\{a_n\}$ is a subsequence of itself.

For example, the subsequence $\{a_{5k+2}\}$ corresponds to the sequence of positive integers

$$n_k = 5k + 2, \quad k = 1, 2, \ldots.$$

The first term of $\{a_{5k+2}\}$ is a_7, the second is a_{12}, and so on.

Note that if $\{n_k\}$ is any strictly increasing sequence of positive integers, then $n_k \geq k$, for $k = 1, 2, \ldots$, so $n_k \to \infty$ as $k \to \infty$.

Exercise 4.4

(a) Let $a_n = n^2$, $n = 1, 2, \ldots$. Write down the first five terms of each of the subsequences $\{a_{n_k}\}$, where:

   (i) $n_k = 2k$;   (ii) $n_k = 4k - 1$;   (iii) $n_k = k^2$.

(b) Write down the first three terms of the odd and even subsequences of the sequence $a_n = n^{(-1)^n}$, $n = 1, 2, \ldots$.

Next we show that certain properties of sequences are inherited by their subsequences.

Theorem 4.2   For any subsequence $\{a_{n_k}\}$ of $\{a_n\}$:

(a) if $a_n \to l$ as $n \to \infty$, then $a_{n_k} \to l$ as $k \to \infty$;

(b) if $a_n \to \infty$ as $n \to \infty$, then $a_{n_k} \to \infty$ as $k \to \infty$.

Proof   To prove part (a), we want to show that

for each positive number ε, there is a positive integer K such that

$$|a_{n_k} - l| < \varepsilon, \quad \text{for all } k > K. \tag{$*$}$$

Let ε be a positive number. Since $\{a_n - l\}$ is null, we know that there is a positive integer N such that

$$|a_n - l| < \varepsilon, \quad \text{for all } n > N.$$

If we take K so large that $n_K \geq N$, then

$$n_k > n_K \geq N, \quad \text{for all } k > K.$$

Hence statement $(*)$ holds, as required.   ■

If you are short of time, omit this proof.
We prove only part (a); the proof of part (b) is similar.

The following criteria for establishing that a sequence is *divergent* are immediate consequences of Theorem 4.2(a).

Corollary

1. **First Subsequence Rule**   The sequence $\{a_n\}$ is divergent if $\{a_n\}$ has two convergent subsequences with different limits.

2. **Second Subsequence Rule**   The sequence $\{a_n\}$ is divergent if $\{a_n\}$ has a subsequence which tends to infinity or a subsequence which tends to minus infinity.

We can now formulate the strategy promised at the beginning of this section.

Strategy 4.1   To prove that the sequence $\{a_n\}$ is divergent:

EITHER

1. show that $\{a_n\}$ has two convergent subsequences with different limits;

OR

2. show that $\{a_n\}$ has a subsequence which tends to infinity or a subsequence which tends to minus infinity.

For example, the sequence $\{(-1)^n\}$ has two subsequences which have different limits, namely, the even subsequences with limit 1 and the odd subsequence with limit -1. So the sequence $\{(-1)^n\}$ is divergent, by the First Subsequence Rule.

On the other hand, the sequence $\{n^{(-1)^n}\}$ has a subsequence (the even subsequence) which tends to infinity. So $\{n^{(-1)^n}\}$ is divergent, by the Second Subsequence Rule.

If $n = 2k$, then
$$n^{(-1)^n} = 2k.$$

Remark   In order to apply Strategy 4.1 successfully to prove that a sequence is divergent, you need to be able to recognise convergent subsequences with different limits, or a subsequence which tends to infinity or to minus infinity. It is not always easy to do this, and some experimentation may be required. If the formula for a_n involves the expression $(-1)^n$, it is a good idea to consider the odd and even subsequences, although this may not always work. It may be helpful to calculate the values of the first few terms in order to try to identify suitable subsequences.

Exercise 4.5   Use Strategy 4.1 to prove that each of the following sequences $\{a_n\}$ is divergent.

(a) $\left\{(-1)^n + \dfrac{1}{n}\right\}$ (b) $\{\frac{1}{3}n - [\frac{1}{3}n]\}$ (c) $\{n\sin(\frac{1}{2}n\pi)\}$

Remember that $[x]$ denotes the integer part of x.

We end this section by giving a result about subsequences which will be needed in later analysis units.

Theorem 4.3   Let $\{a_n\}$ consist of two subsequences $\{a_{m_k}\}$ and $\{a_{n_k}\}$, which both tend to the *same* limit l. Then

$$\lim_{n \to \infty} a_n = l.$$

For example, we can apply Theorem 4.3 with the odd and even subsequences, $\{a_{2k-1}\}$ and $\{a_{2k}\}$, of $\{a_n\}$.

Proof   We want to show that

for each $\varepsilon > 0$, there is an integer N such that

$$|a_n - l| < \varepsilon, \quad \text{for all } n > N. \tag{$*$}$$

Let ε be a positive number. We know that there are integers K_1 and K_2 such that

$$|a_{m_k} - l| < \varepsilon, \quad \text{for all } k > K_1,$$

and

$$|a_{n_k} - l| < \varepsilon, \quad \text{for all } k > K_2.$$

Now let

$$N = \max\{m_{K_1}, n_{K_2}\}.$$

Since each $n > N$ is either of the form m_k, with $k > K_1$, or of the form n_k, with $k > K_2$, we deduce that statement $(*)$ holds with this value of N.   ∎

Further exercises

Exercise 4.6   Classify the following sequences as bounded or unbounded and as convergent or divergent.

(a) $\{n^{1/4}\}$ (b) $\{100^n/n!\}$

Exercise 4.7   Use the Reciprocal Rule to prove that the following sequences tend to infinity.

(a) $\{n!/n^3\}$ (b) $\{n^2 + 2n\}$ (c) $\{n^2 - 2n\}$ (d) $\{n! - n^3 - 3^n\}$

Exercise 4.8   Use the Subsequence Rules to prove that the following sequences are divergent.

(a) $\{(-1)^n 2^n\}$ (b) $\left\{\dfrac{(-1)^n n^2}{2n^2 + 1}\right\}$

5 Monotone Convergence Theorem

After working through this section, you should be able to:

(a) state the Monotone Convergence Theorem;

(b) understand the role of the Monotone Convergence Theorem in the definitions of the numbers π and e.

This section contains the video section. First we introduce the Monotone Convergence Theorem, which plays a key role in the video programme and also in later analysis units.

5.1 Monotonic sequences

In Section 3 we gave various techniques for finding the limit of a convergent sequence. As a result, you may be under the impression that if we know that a sequence converges, then we can always find its limit. However, it is sometimes possible to prove that a sequence is convergent, without being able to find its limit. For example, this situation can occur with a given sequence $\{a_n\}$ which has the following two properties:

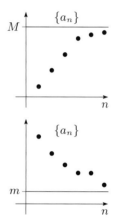

1. $\{a_n\}$ is an *increasing* sequence;

2. $\{a_n\}$ is *bounded above*; that is, there is a real number M such that

$$a_n \le M, \quad \text{for } n = 1, 2, \ldots.$$

Likewise, if $\{a_n\}$ is a sequence which is *decreasing* and *bounded below*, then $\{a_n\}$ must be convergent.

We combine these two results into one statement.

Theorem 5.1 Monotone Convergence Theorem

If the sequence $\{a_n\}$ is:

EITHER   increasing and bounded above,

OR   decreasing and bounded below,

then $\{a_n\}$ is convergent.

We suggest that you read the proof of this theorem after watching the video.

We prove only the increasing version; the proof of the decreasing version is similar.

Proof   Since $\{a_n\}$ is bounded above, the set $\{a_n : n = 1, 2, \ldots\}$ has a least upper bound, l say. This is true by the Least Upper Bound Property of $\mathbb{R}$. We now prove that

See Unit AA1, Section 4.

$$\lim_{n \to \infty} a_n = l.$$

We want to show that

for each $\varepsilon > 0$, there is an integer N such that

$$|a_n - l| < \varepsilon, \quad \text{for all } n > N. \tag{$*$}$$

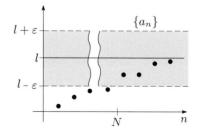

Let ε be a positive number. Since l is the least upper bound of the set $\{a_n : n = 1, 2, \ldots\}$, there is an integer N such that

$$a_N > l - \varepsilon.$$

Because $\{a_n\}$ is increasing, we have $a_n \ge a_N$ for $n > N$, so

$$a_n > l - \varepsilon, \quad \text{for all } n > N.$$

Thus,

$$|a_n - l| = l - a_n < \varepsilon, \quad \text{for all } n > N,$$

which proves statement $(*)$. Hence $\{a_n\}$ converges to l. ∎

Here $|a_n - l| = l - a_n$ because $a_n \le l$.

The Monotone Convergence Theorem tells us that a sequence such as $\{1 - 1/n\}$, which is increasing and bounded above (by 1, for example), must be convergent. In this case we already know that $\{1 - 1/n\}$ is convergent, with limit 1, without using the Monotone Convergence Theorem.

The Monotone Convergence Theorem is often used when we suspect that a sequence is convergent, but we cannot find the limit directly. It can also be used to give precise definitions of numbers, such as π, about which we have only an informal idea, and we do this in the video.

For completeness, we point out that if $\{a_n\}$ is increasing but is not bounded above, then $a_n \to \infty$. For if $\{a_n\}$ is not bounded above then, for any real number M, we can find an integer N such that $a_N > M$. Since $\{a_n\}$ is increasing, we have $a_n \ge a_N$ for $n > N$, so

$$a_n > M, \quad \text{for all } n > N.$$

Hence $a_n \to \infty$ as $n \to \infty$.

Similarly, if $\{a_n\}$ is decreasing but is not bounded below, then $a_n \to -\infty$.

We now summarise all these results about monotonic sequences.

Theorem 5.2 Monotonic Sequence Theorem

If the sequence $\{a_n\}$ is monotonic, then

EITHER $\{a_n\}$ is convergent

OR $a_n \to \pm\infty$.

Before watching the video, you should try the following exercise.

Exercise 5.1   Verify that the following triangles have the stated areas.

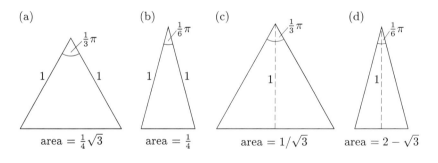

(a) $\frac{1}{3}\pi$ 1 1 area $= \frac{1}{4}\sqrt{3}$

(b) $\frac{1}{6}\pi$ 1 1 area $= \frac{1}{4}$

(c) $\frac{1}{3}\pi$ 1 area $= 1/\sqrt{3}$

(d) $\frac{1}{6}\pi$ 1 area $= 2 - \sqrt{3}$

Here π is used to represent angles; its value is not required in calculating the areas of the triangles.

Hint: In part (d) use the half-angle formula $\tan\theta = \dfrac{2\tan\frac{1}{2}\theta}{1 - \tan^2\frac{1}{2}\theta}$.

Watch the video programme 'π and e'.

Video

5.2 Review of the video programme

The number π

One of the oldest mathematical problems is to determine the area of a disc of radius r and the length of its perimeter. It is well known that these magnitudes are given by the formulas πr^2 and $2\pi r$, respectively. But what exactly is π?

In the video we define π by giving a precise definition of the area of a disc of radius 1. Our definition is based on a method used by Archimedes to approximate a circle of radius 1 by regular polygons with 6 sides, 12 sides, 24 sides, and so on, inscribed in the circle. The areas of such polygons can be calculated quite simply. The solutions to Exercise 5.1(a) and (b) give the first two of these areas.

Archimedes of Syracuse (c. 287–212 BC) was a Greek mathematician and scientist. He used this method to show that
$$3\tfrac{10}{71} < \pi < 3\tfrac{1}{7}.$$

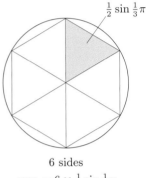

$\frac{1}{2}\sin\frac{1}{3}\pi$

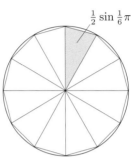

$\frac{1}{2}\sin\frac{1}{6}\pi$

6 sides
$$\begin{aligned} \text{area} &= 6 \times \tfrac{1}{2}\sin\tfrac{1}{3}\pi \\ &= 6 \times \tfrac{1}{4}\sqrt{3} \\ &\simeq 2.598 \end{aligned}$$

12 sides
$$\begin{aligned} \text{area} &= 12 \times \tfrac{1}{2}\sin\tfrac{1}{6}\pi \\ &= 12 \times \tfrac{1}{4} \\ &= 3 \end{aligned}$$

Let s_n denote the number of sides of the nth such inner polygon, so $s_1 = 6$, $s_2 = 12$ and, in general, $s_n = 3 \times 2^n$. The nth inner polygon consists of s_n isosceles triangles, each with two equal sides of length 1 and included angle $2\pi/s_n$. Thus its total area a_n is given by

$$a_n = \tfrac{1}{2}s_n\sin(2\pi/s_n), \quad \text{for } n = 1, 2, \ldots. \tag{5.1}$$

Geometrically, it is clear that each time we double the number of sides of the inner polygon, the area increases, so

$$a_1 < a_2 < a_3 < \cdots < a_n < a_{n+1} < \cdots.$$

Hence the sequence $\{a_n\}$ is (strictly) increasing.

For example (to 3 d.p.),
$$a_1 = 2.598,$$
$$a_2 = 3,$$
$$\vdots$$
$$a_6 = 3.141.$$

Note that each of the polygons lies inside a square of side 2, which has area 4. This implies that

$$a_n \le 4, \quad \text{for } n = 1, 2, \ldots.$$

Thus the sequence $\{a_n\}$ is bounded above by 4.

Hence, by the Monotone Convergence Theorem, the sequence $\{a_n\}$ is convergent, with limit at most 4. Our intuitive idea of the area of the disc suggests that it is greater than each of the areas a_n, but 'only just'. This leads us to make the following definition.

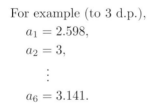

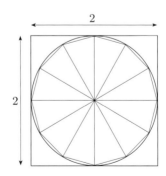

Definition $\pi = \lim\limits_{n\to\infty} a_n$.

We shall explain in a moment how to calculate the terms a_n without assuming a value for π.

First, however, we describe how to estimate the area of the disc using *outer* polygons. Once again we start with a regular hexagon and repeatedly double the number of sides. The solutions to Exercise 5.1(c) and (d) give the first two of these areas.

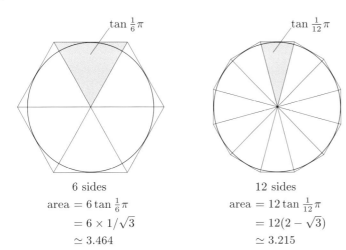

6 sides

area $= 6\tan\frac{1}{6}\pi$

$= 6 \times 1/\sqrt{3}$

$\simeq 3.464$

12 sides

area $= 12\tan\frac{1}{12}\pi$

$= 12(2-\sqrt{3})$

$\simeq 3.215$

As before, let $s_n = 3 \times 2^n$, for $n = 1, 2, \ldots$, and let b_n denote the area of the nth outer polygon. This nth outer polygon consists of s_n isosceles triangles, each of height 1 and base $2\tan(\pi/s_n)$. Thus

$$b_n = s_n \tan(\pi/s_n), \quad n = 1, 2, \ldots. \tag{5.2}$$

Geometrically, it is clear that, each time we double the number of sides of the outer polygon, the area decreases, so

$$b_1 > b_2 > b_3 > \cdots > b_n > b_{n+1} > \cdots.$$

Hence the sequence $\{b_n\}$ is (strictly) decreasing and bounded below (by 0, for example). Thus, by the Monotone Convergence Theorem, $\{b_n\}$ is also convergent. Intuitively, we expect that $\{b_n\}$ has the same limit as $\{a_n\}$, which we have defined to be π. But how can we prove this?

It is a remarkable fact that the terms a_n and b_n can be calculated by using the following equations, known as the *Archimedean algorithm*:

$$a_{n+1} = \sqrt{a_n b_n}, \quad n = 1, 2, \ldots, \tag{5.3}$$

$$b_{n+1} = \frac{2a_{n+1}b_n}{a_{n+1} + b_n}, \quad n = 1, 2, \ldots. \tag{5.4}$$

Starting with $a_1 = \frac{3}{2}\sqrt{3} = 2.598\ldots$ and $b_1 = 2\sqrt{3} = 3.464\ldots$, we can use these equations iteratively to calculate first $a_2 = \sqrt{a_1 b_1}$, then $b_2 = 2a_2 b_1/(a_2 + b_1)$, and so on. Here are the first few values (to 3 decimal places) of each sequence obtained in this way.

s_n	6	12	24	48	96	192
a_n	2.598	3	3.106	3.133	3.139	3.141
b_n	3.464	3.215	3.160	3.146	3.143	3.142

It appears that the sequence $\{b_n\}$ converges to the same limit as $\{a_n\}$. Indeed, by equation (5.3), we have $b_n = a_{n+1}^2/a_n$, so

$$\lim_{n\to\infty} b_n = \frac{\left(\lim\limits_{n\to\infty} a_{n+1}\right)^2}{\lim\limits_{n\to\infty} a_n} = \frac{\pi^2}{\pi} = \pi,$$

by the Combination Rules and our definition of π.

For example (to 3 d.p.),

$b_1 = 3.464,$

$b_2 = 3.215,$

$\vdots$

$b_6 = 3.142.$

These equations for calculating a_n and b_n can be deduced from equations (5.1) and (5.2) by using trigonometric identities. We omit the details.

41

However, the convergence of these sequences $\{a_n\}$ and $\{b_n\}$ to $\pi = 3.14159\ldots$ seems quite slow.

Remark   We have defined π using the *areas* of approximating polygons. Archimedes' original method used the *perimeters* of these polygons; the details are similar.

In Unit AB4 we give other ways to calculate π, which are more efficient, and we show that π is an irrational number.

The number e

In the second part of the video we prove that

$$\lim_{n\to\infty}\left(1+\frac{1}{n}\right)^n$$

exists and we define this limit to be e.

To show that $\{(1+1/n)^n\}$ is convergent using the Monotone Convergence Theorem, we prove that this sequence is increasing and bounded above. If we plot the first few terms of the sequence $\{(1+1/n)^n\}$ on a sequence diagram, then it certainly seems that these properties hold.

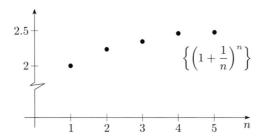

We prove these facts by using the Binomial Theorem:

$$\left(1+\frac{1}{n}\right)^n = 1 + n\left(\frac{1}{n}\right) + \frac{n(n-1)}{2!}\left(\frac{1}{n}\right)^2 + \cdots + \left(\frac{1}{n}\right)^n.$$

As n increases, the number of terms in this sum increases and the new terms are all positive. Also, for each fixed $k \geq 1$ and any $n \geq k$, the $(k+1)$th term of the sum is

$$\frac{n(n-1)\cdots(n-k+1)}{k!}\left(\frac{1}{n}\right)^k$$

$$= \frac{1}{k!}\left(1-\frac{1}{n}\right)\left(1-\frac{2}{n}\right)\cdots\left(1-\frac{k-1}{n}\right),$$

and the product on the right increases as n increases (because each of the factors does). Hence the sequence $\{(1+1/n)^n\}$ is increasing.

To see that this sequence is bounded above, note that the $(k+1)$th term of the above sum satisfies the inequality

$$\frac{1}{k!}\left(1-\frac{1}{n}\right)\left(1-\frac{2}{n}\right)\cdots\left(1-\frac{k-1}{n}\right) \leq \frac{1}{k!},$$

since each of the expressions in brackets is at most 1. Hence

$$\left(1+\frac{1}{n}\right)^n \leq 1 + 1 + \frac{1}{2!} + \frac{1}{3!} + \cdots + \frac{1}{n!}$$

$$\leq 1 + 1 + \frac{1}{2^1} + \frac{1}{2^2} + \cdots + \frac{1}{2^{n-1}},$$

since $k! = k(k-1) \times \cdots \times 2 \times 1 \geq 2^{k-1}$, for $k = 1, 2, \ldots$.

Now

$$1 + \frac{1}{2^1} + \frac{1}{2^2} + \cdots + \frac{1}{2^{n-1}} = 2 - \frac{1}{2^{n-1}},$$

so

$$\left(1 + \frac{1}{n}\right)^n \le 3 - \frac{1}{2^{n-1}}, \quad \text{for } n = 1, 2, \ldots.$$

Here we use the sum of a finite geometric series

$$1 + r + \cdots + r^{n-1} = \frac{1 - r^n}{1 - r},$$

in the case $r = \frac{1}{2}$.

Thus the sequence $\{(1 + 1/n)^n\}$ is bounded above by 3.

Hence, by the Monotone Convergence Theorem, the sequence $\{(1 + 1/n)^n\}$ is convergent, with limit at most 3. This allows us to make the following definition.

Definition $e = \lim\limits_{n \to \infty} \left(1 + \dfrac{1}{n}\right)^n.$

For larger and larger values of n, the terms $(1 + 1/n)^n$ give better and better approximate values for e. However, the sequence $\{(1 + 1/n)^n\}$ converges to e rather slowly, and we need to take very large integers n to get a reasonable approximation to $e = 2.718\,28\ldots$.

Next we discuss the equation

$$e^x = \lim_{n \to \infty} \left(1 + \frac{x}{n}\right)^n. \tag{5.5}$$

For example,

$$(1 + \tfrac{1}{1000})^{1000} = 2.716\ldots.$$

In Unit AA3 we give another way to calculate e, which is more efficient, and we show that e is an irrational number.

In the video we show that equation (5.5) holds for $x = 2$; that is,

$$\lim_{n \to \infty} \left(1 + \frac{2}{n}\right)^n = e^2.$$

To do this we write $(1 + 2/n)^n$ in the form

$$\left(1 + \frac{2}{n}\right)^n = \left(\frac{n+2}{n}\right)^n = \left(\frac{n+2}{n+1}\right)^n \left(\frac{n+1}{n}\right)^n.$$

We know that

$$\lim_{n \to \infty} \left(\frac{n+1}{n}\right)^n = \lim_{n \to \infty} \left(1 + \frac{1}{n}\right)^n = e.$$

Also, by the Quotient Rule,

$$\lim_{n \to \infty} \left(\frac{n+2}{n+1}\right)^n = \lim_{n \to \infty} \left(1 + \frac{1}{n+1}\right)^n$$

$$= \lim_{n \to \infty} \left(\left(1 + \frac{1}{n+1}\right)^{n+1} \Big/ \left(1 + \frac{1}{n+1}\right)\right)$$

$$= \lim_{n \to \infty} \left(1 + \frac{1}{n+1}\right)^{n+1} \Big/ \lim_{n \to \infty} \left(1 + \frac{1}{n+1}\right)$$

$$= e/1 = e.$$

Thus, by the Product Rule,

$$\lim_{n \to \infty} \left(1 + \frac{2}{n}\right)^n = \lim_{n \to \infty} \left(\frac{n+2}{n+1}\right)^n \left(\frac{n+1}{n}\right)^n = e^2.$$

A similar argument serves to show that equation (5.5) holds with $x = 3, 4, 5, \ldots$. More generally, it can be shown that equation (5.5) holds for any *rational* number x. Clearly, then, we would like to prove that equation (5.5) holds also when x is *irrational*.

The example $x = \frac{3}{2}$ is in the post-programme work.

See the discussion of rational powers in Unit AA1, Section 5.

The problem is that we have not yet defined the expression e^x if x is irrational. Instead, we can use equation (5.5) as the *definition* of e^x when x is irrational. For example, we define e^π by the statement

$$e^\pi = \lim_{n \to \infty} \left(1 + \frac{\pi}{n}\right)^n.$$

This definition is justified only if we can prove that the limit on the right exists, and we ask you to do this (for $x > 0$) in the post-programme work.

5.3 Post-programme work

Exercise 5.2 Suppose that $x > 0$.

(a) Prove that $\{(1 + x/n)^n\}$ is an increasing sequence by adapting the method used in the video programme for the case $x = 1$.

(b) Prove that the sequence $\{(1 + x/n)^n\}$ is bounded above.

Hint: Choose an integer $k \geq x$ and use the inequality

$$1 + \frac{k}{n} \leq \left(1 + \frac{1}{n}\right)^k, \quad \text{for } k = 1, 2, \ldots.$$

This inequality follows from the Binomial Theorem.

(c) Deduce that if $x > 0$, then $\{(1 + x/n)^n\}$ is convergent.

Exercise 5.3 Assuming that $\lim_{n \to \infty} (1 + 3/n)^n = e^3$, deduce that

$$\lim_{n \to \infty} \left(1 + \frac{3/2}{n}\right)^n = e^{3/2}.$$

Hint: Consider the sequence

$$\left(1 + \frac{3}{2n}\right)^{2n}, \quad n = 1, 2, \ldots.$$

Further exercises

Exercise 5.4 Prove that if the sequence $\{a_n\}$ is increasing and has a subsequence $\{a_{n_k}\}$ which is convergent, then $\{a_n\}$ is convergent.

Exercise 5.5 Prove that

$$n! > \left(\frac{n+1}{e}\right)^n, \quad \text{for } n = 1, 2, \ldots.$$

Hint: Consider the product of the first n terms of the sequence $\{(1 + 1/n)^n\}$.

Solutions to the exercises

1.1 (a) (i) $4, 7, 10, 13, 16.$

(ii) $\frac{1}{3}, \frac{1}{9}, \frac{1}{27}, \frac{1}{81}, \frac{1}{243}.$

(iii) $-1, 2, -3, 4, -5.$

(b) (i) $a_1 = 1$, $a_2 = 2$, $a_3 = 6$, $a_4 = 24$, $a_5 = 120.$

(ii) $a_1 = 2$, $a_2 = 2.25$, $a_3 = 2.37$, $a_4 = 2.44$, $a_5 = 2.49.$

1.2 (a)

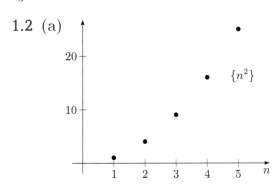

(b)

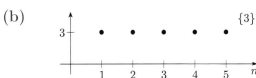

(c)

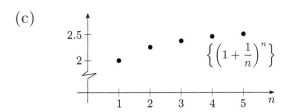

(d)

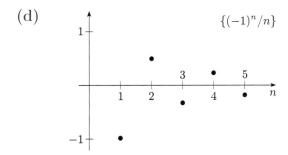

1.3 (a) Since $a_n > 0$ for all n, we can use Strategy 1.2. We have
$$a_n = n! \quad \text{and} \quad a_{n+1} = (n+1)!,$$
so
$$\frac{a_{n+1}}{a_n} = \frac{(n+1)!}{n!}$$
$$= n+1 \geq 1, \quad \text{for } 1, 2, \ldots.$$
Thus $\{n!\}$ is increasing, so $\{n!\}$ is monotonic.

(b) Since $a_n > 0$ for all n, we can use Strategy 1.2. We have
$$a_n = 2^{-n} \quad \text{and} \quad a_{n+1} = 2^{-(n+1)},$$
so
$$\frac{a_{n+1}}{a_n} = \frac{2^n}{2^{n+1}} = \frac{1}{2} < 1, \quad \text{for } n = 1, 2, \ldots.$$
Thus $\{2^{-n}\}$ is decreasing, so $\{2^{-n}\}$ is monotonic.

(c) We use Strategy 1.1. We have
$$a_n = n + \frac{1}{n} \quad \text{and} \quad a_{n+1} = n + 1 + \frac{1}{n+1},$$
so
$$a_{n+1} - a_n = \left(n + 1 + \frac{1}{n+1}\right) - \left(n + \frac{1}{n}\right)$$
$$= \frac{n(n+1) - 1}{n(n+1)} \geq 0, \quad \text{for } n = 1, 2, \ldots.$$
Thus $\{n + 1/n\}$ is increasing, so $\{n + 1/n\}$ is monotonic.

1.4 (a) True: $2^n > 1000$, for $n > 9$, since $\{2^n\}$ is increasing and $2^{10} = 1024.$

(b) False: all the terms $a_1, a_3, a_5, \ldots$ are negative.

(c) True: $\frac{1}{n} < 0.025$, for $n > \frac{1}{0.025} = 40.$

(d) True: $a_n > 0$ for all n, and
$$\frac{a_{n+1}}{a_n} = \frac{1}{4}\left(\frac{n+1}{n}\right)^4.$$
Now
$$\frac{1}{4}\left(\frac{n+1}{n}\right)^4 \leq 1 \Leftrightarrow \left(\frac{n+1}{n}\right)^4 \leq 4$$
$$\Leftrightarrow 1 + \frac{1}{n} \leq 4^{1/4}$$
$$\Leftrightarrow \frac{1}{n} \leq \sqrt{2} - 1$$
$$\Leftrightarrow n \geq (\sqrt{2} - 1)^{-1} \simeq 2.414.$$
So
$$\frac{a_{n+1}}{a_n} \leq 1, \quad \text{for } n > 2.$$
Hence
$$a_{n+1} \leq a_n, \quad \text{for } n > 2,$$
so $\{n^4/4^n\}$ is eventually decreasing.

1.5 (a) $1, 0, 1, 4, 9.$

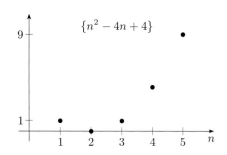

(b) $1, -\frac{1}{2}, \frac{1}{6}, -\frac{1}{24}, \frac{1}{120}.$

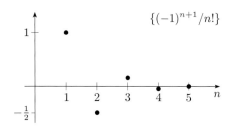

(c) $\dfrac{1}{\sqrt{2}}, 1, \dfrac{1}{\sqrt{2}}, 0, -\dfrac{1}{\sqrt{2}}.$

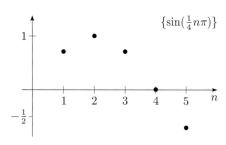

1.6 (a) Let $a_n = \dfrac{n}{n+1}$, so $a_{n+1} = \dfrac{n+1}{n+2}$.
Since $a_n > 0$ for all n, we can use Strategy 1.2. We have

$$\frac{a_{n+1}}{a_n} = \frac{(n+1)/(n+2)}{n/(n+1)}$$

$$= \frac{n^2 + 2n + 1}{n^2 + 2n} \geq 1, \quad \text{for } n = 1, 2, \ldots.$$

Hence $\{a_n\}$ is increasing, so $\{a_n\}$ is monotonic.

(b) Let $a_n = (-1)^n/n$. Then

$$a_1 = -1, \ a_2 = \tfrac{1}{2}, \ a_3 = -\tfrac{1}{3}.$$

Since $a_1 < a_2$, we know that $\{a_n\}$ is not decreasing; and since $a_3 < a_2$, we know that $\{a_n\}$ is not increasing.

Hence $\{a_n\}$ is not monotonic.

(c) Let $a_n = 2^{1/n}$, so $a_{n+1} = 2^{1/(n+1)}$. Then

$$a_{n+1} = 2^{1/(n+1)} \leq 2^{1/n} = a_n, \quad \text{for } n = 1, 2, \ldots.$$

This holds because, by the rules for inequalities (Rule 5 with $p = n(n+1)$),

$$2^{1/(n+1)} \leq 2^{1/n} \iff 2^n \leq 2^{n+1},$$

and the right-hand inequality is true for $n = 1, 2, \ldots$. Hence $\{a_n\}$ is decreasing, so $\{a_n\}$ is monotonic.

1.7 (a) Let $a_n = 5^n/n!$. Then $a_n > 0$ for all n and

$$\frac{a_{n+1}}{a_n} = \frac{5^{n+1}/(n+1)!}{5^n/n!} = \frac{5}{n+1}.$$

Now

$$\frac{5}{n+1} \leq 1, \quad \text{for } n = 4, 5, 6, \ldots,$$

so

$$a_{n+1} \leq a_n, \quad \text{for } n = 4, 5, 6, \ldots.$$

Hence $\{a_n\}$ is eventually decreasing.

(b) Let $a_n = \{n + 8/n\}$. Then

$$a_{n+1} - a_n = \left(n + 1 + \frac{8}{n+1}\right) - \left(n + \frac{8}{n}\right)$$

$$= 1 - \frac{8}{n(n+1)}.$$

Now

$$\frac{8}{n(n+1)} \leq 1 \iff n(n+1) \geq 8$$

and this final inequality holds for $n \geq 3$. Hence

$$a_{n+1} \geq a_n, \quad \text{for } n \geq 3,$$

so $\{a_n\}$ is eventually increasing.

2.3 (a) The sequence $\{1/(2n-1)\}$ is a null sequence. To prove this, we want to show that:

for each $\varepsilon > 0$, there is an integer N such that

$$\frac{1}{2n-1} < \varepsilon, \quad \text{for all } n > N. \tag{$*$}$$

We know that

$$\frac{1}{2n-1} < \varepsilon \iff 2n - 1 > \frac{1}{\varepsilon}$$

$$\iff n > \tfrac{1}{2}\left(1 + \frac{1}{\varepsilon}\right),$$

so statement $(*)$ holds if we take $N = \left[\tfrac{1}{2}(1 + 1/\varepsilon)\right]$. Hence $\{1/(2n-1)\}$ is null.

(b) The sequence $\{(-1)^n/10\}$ is not a null sequence. To prove this, we must find a positive value of ε such that the sequence does not eventually lie in the horizontal strip on the sequence diagram from $-\varepsilon$ to ε. If we take $\varepsilon = \frac{1}{20}$, then no terms of the sequence lie in this strip, as you can see in the following sequence diagram.

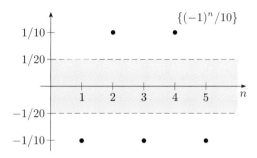

Thus there is no value of N such that the statement
$$\left|\frac{(-1)^n}{10}\right| < \tfrac{1}{20}, \quad \text{for all } n > N,$$
is true.

(c) The sequence $\left\{\dfrac{(-1)^n}{n^4+1}\right\}$ is a null sequence.

To prove this, we want to show that:

for each $\varepsilon > 0$, there is an integer N such that
$$\left|\frac{(-1)^n}{n^4+1}\right| < \varepsilon, \quad \text{for all } n > N. \tag{$*$}$$

We know that
$$\left|\frac{(-1)^n}{n^4+1}\right| = \frac{1}{n^4+1}, \quad \text{for } n = 1, 2, \ldots,$$
and
$$\frac{1}{n^4+1} < \varepsilon \Leftrightarrow n^4 + 1 > \frac{1}{\varepsilon}$$
$$\Leftrightarrow n^4 > \frac{1}{\varepsilon} - 1.$$

Now $\dfrac{1}{\varepsilon} - 1$ is sometimes positive and sometimes negative, so we need to consider two cases.

If $\varepsilon \geq 1$, then $\dfrac{1}{\varepsilon} - 1 \leq 0$, so
$$n^4 > \frac{1}{\varepsilon} - 1, \quad \text{for } n = 1, 2, \ldots.$$
Hence statement $(*)$ holds with $N = 1$.

If $0 < \varepsilon < 1$, then $\dfrac{1}{\varepsilon} - 1 > 0$, so
$$n^4 > \frac{1}{\varepsilon} - 1 \Leftrightarrow n > \left(\frac{1}{\varepsilon} - 1\right)^{1/4}.$$
Hence statement $(*)$ holds if we take $N = \left[(1/\varepsilon - 1)^{1/4}\right]$.

Thus statement $(*)$ holds in either case, so $\left\{\dfrac{(-1)^n}{n^4+1}\right\}$ is null.

2.4 (a) We know that $\{1/(2n-1)\}$ is null, so $\{1/(2n-1)^3\}$ is null, by the Power Rule.

(b) The sequences $\{1/n\}$ and $\{1/(2n-1)\}$ are null, so $\{6/\sqrt[5]{n}\}$ and $\{5/(2n-1)^7\}$ are null, by the Power Rule and the Multiple Rule.

Hence $\{6/\sqrt[5]{n} + 5/(2n-1)^7\}$ is null, by the Sum Rule.

(c) The sequences $\{1/n\}$ and $\{1/(2n-1)\}$ are null, so $\{1/n^4\}$ and $\{1/(2n-1)^{1/3}\}$ are also null, by the Power Rule.

Hence $\{1/\left(3n^4(2n-1)^{1/3}\right)\}$ is null, by the Product Rule and the Multiple Rule.

2.5 (a) We guess that $\{1/(n^2+n)\}$ is dominated by $\{1/n\}$. To check this, we have to show that
$$\frac{1}{n^2+n} \leq \frac{1}{n}, \quad \text{for } n = 1, 2, \ldots.$$
This holds because
$$n^2 + n \geq n, \quad \text{for } n = 1, 2, \ldots.$$
Since $\{1/n\}$ is null, we deduce that $\{1/(n^2+n)\}$ is null, by the Squeeze Rule.

(b) We guess that $\{(-1)^n/n!\}$ is dominated by $\{1/n\}$. To check this, we have to show that
$$\left|\frac{(-1)^n}{n!}\right| \leq \frac{1}{n}, \quad \text{for } n = 1, 2, \ldots.$$
This holds because
$$\left|\frac{(-1)^n}{n!}\right| = \frac{1}{n!}$$
and
$$n! \geq n, \quad \text{for } n = 1, 2, \ldots.$$
Since $\{1/n\}$ is null, we deduce that $\{(-1)^n/n!\}$ is null, by the Squeeze Rule.

(c) We guess that $\{\sin(n^2)/(n^2+2^n)\}$ is dominated by $\{1/n^2\}$. To check this, we have to show that
$$\left|\frac{\sin(n^2)}{n^2+2^n}\right| \leq \frac{1}{n^2}, \quad \text{for } n = 1, 2, \ldots.$$
This holds because $|\sin(n^2)| \leq 1$ and
$$n^2 + 2^n \geq n^2, \quad \text{for } n = 1, 2, \ldots.$$
Since $\{1/n^2\}$ is null, we deduce, by the Squeeze Rule, that $\{\sin(n^2)/(n^2+2^n)\}$ is null.

2.6 (a) Since $|a_n| = \left|\dfrac{(-1)^n}{n^5}\right| = \dfrac{1}{n^5}$, we have
$$|a_n| < 0.001 \Leftrightarrow n^5 > 1000$$
$$\Leftrightarrow n > 1000^{1/5} \simeq 3.98.$$
Hence
$$|a_n| < 0.001, \quad \text{for all } n > 3,$$
so we can take $N = 3$.

(b) Since $|a_n| = 1/(2n+1)^2$, we have
$$|a_n| < 0.002 \iff (2n+1)^2 > 500$$
$$\iff n > \tfrac{1}{2}(\sqrt{500} - 1) \simeq 10.68.$$
Hence
$$|a_n| < 0.002, \quad \text{for all } n > 10,$$
so we can take $N = 10$.

2.7 (a) We want to show that:

for each $\varepsilon > 0$, there is an integer N such that
$$\left| \frac{(-1)^n}{n^5} \right| = \frac{1}{n^5} < \varepsilon, \quad \text{for all } n > N. \qquad (*)$$
We know that
$$\frac{1}{n^5} < \varepsilon \iff n^5 > \frac{1}{\varepsilon}$$
$$\iff n > \left(\frac{1}{\varepsilon} \right)^{1/5}.$$
If we take $N = [(1/\varepsilon)^{1/5}]$, then statement $(*)$ holds. Hence $\{(-1)^n/n^5\}$ is null.

(b) We want to show that:

for each $\varepsilon > 0$, there is an integer N such that
$$\frac{1}{(2n+1)^2} < \varepsilon, \quad \text{for all } n > N. \qquad (*)$$
We know that
$$\frac{1}{(2n+1)^2} < \varepsilon \iff (2n+1)^2 > 1/\varepsilon$$
$$\iff n > \tfrac{1}{2}\left(\sqrt{1/\varepsilon} - 1 \right).$$
We consider two cases.

If $\varepsilon \geq 1$, then $\tfrac{1}{2}(\sqrt{1/\varepsilon} - 1) \leq 0$, so $n > \tfrac{1}{2}(\sqrt{1/\varepsilon} - 1)$, for $n = 1, 2, \ldots$, and hence statement $(*)$ holds with $N = 1$.

If $0 < \varepsilon < 1$, then statement $(*)$ holds if we take $N = [\tfrac{1}{2}(\sqrt{1/\varepsilon} - 1)]$.

Thus statement $(*)$ holds in either case, so $\{1/(2n+1)^2\}$ is null.

2.8 (a) We have to find a positive number ε such that the sequence $\{\sqrt{n}\}$ does not lie eventually in the horizontal strip from $-\varepsilon$ to ε.

Since $\sqrt{n} > \tfrac{1}{2}$ for all n, we can take $\varepsilon = \tfrac{1}{2}$.

(b) We have to find a positive number ε such that the sequence $\{1 + (-1)^n/n\}$ does not lie eventually in the horizontal strip from $-\varepsilon$ to ε.

Since
$$\left| \frac{(-1)^n}{n} \right| = \frac{1}{n} \leq \tfrac{1}{2} \quad \text{for } n \geq 2,$$
we have
$$-\tfrac{1}{2} \leq \frac{(-1)^n}{n} \leq \tfrac{1}{2}. \quad \text{for } n \geq 2,$$
so
$$\tfrac{1}{2} \leq 1 + \frac{(-1)^n}{n} \leq \tfrac{3}{2}, \quad \text{for } n \geq 2.$$

Thus the terms of $\{1 + (-1)^n/n\}$ do not eventually lie in the strip from $-\tfrac{1}{2}$ to $\tfrac{1}{2}$, so we can take $\varepsilon = \tfrac{1}{2}$.

2.9 (a) The sequences $\left\{ \dfrac{2}{\sqrt{n}} \right\}$ and $\left\{ \dfrac{3}{n^7} \right\}$ are null, by the Power Rule and the Multiple Rule.

Hence $\left\{ \dfrac{2}{\sqrt{n}} + \dfrac{3}{n^7} \right\}$ is null, by the Sum Rule.

(b) Since $|\cos n| \leq 1$, for $n = 1, 2, \ldots$, and
$$n^2 + 1 \geq n \quad \text{for } n = 1, 2, \ldots,$$
we have
$$\left| \frac{\cos n}{n^2 + 1} \right| \leq \frac{1}{n}, \quad \text{for } n = 1, 2, \ldots.$$
Hence $\left\{ \dfrac{\cos n}{n^2 + 1} \right\}$ is null, by the Squeeze Rule.

(c) Since
$$\frac{n!}{n^n} = \frac{1 \times 2 \times \cdots \times n}{n \times n \times \cdots \times n} = \frac{1}{n} \times \frac{2}{n} \times \cdots \times \frac{n}{n},$$
we have
$$0 \leq \frac{n!}{n^n} \leq \frac{1}{n}, \quad \text{for } n = 1, 2, \ldots.$$
Hence $\{n!/n^n\}$ is null, by the Squeeze Rule.

2.10 Using the given identity, we obtain
$$\sqrt{n+1} - \sqrt{n} = ((n+1) - n)/(\sqrt{n+1} + \sqrt{n}).$$
Thus, for $n = 1, 2, \ldots$, we have
$$0 \leq \sqrt{n+1} - \sqrt{n} = \frac{1}{\sqrt{n+1} + \sqrt{n}} \leq \frac{1}{2\sqrt{n}}.$$
Now $\{1/(2\sqrt{n})\}$ is null, by the Power Rule and the Multiple Rule.

Hence $\{\sqrt{n+1} - \sqrt{n}\}$ is null, by the Squeeze Rule.

2.11 (a) Both $\{1/4^n\} = \{(1/4)^n\}$ and $\{n/3^n\} = \{n(1/3)^n\}$ are basic null sequences, so
$$\left\{ \frac{3}{4^n} + \frac{2n}{3^n} \right\}$$
is a null sequence, by the Multiple Rule and the Sum Rule.

(b) $\{n^{10}/n!\}$ is a basic null sequence, so $\{6n^{10}/n!\}$ is a null sequence, by the Multiple Rule.

(c) First note that
$$\frac{n^{10}10^n}{n!} = \left(\frac{n^{10}}{10^n} \right) \left(\frac{100^n}{n!} \right), \quad \text{for } n = 1, 2, \ldots.$$
Since $\{n^{10}/10^n\}$ and $\{100^n/n!\}$ are basic null sequences, $\{n^{10}10^n/n!\}$ is null, by the Product Rule.

3.1 (a)

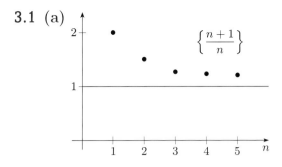

The sequence appears to converge to 1.

(b) $b_n = a_n - 1 = \dfrac{n+1}{n} - 1 = \dfrac{1}{n}$.

Hence $\{b_n\} = \{1/n\}$ is a null sequence.

3.2 We have
$$a_n - \frac{1}{2} = \frac{n^3+1}{2n^3} - \frac{1}{2} = \frac{1}{2n^3}.$$
We know that $\{1/(2n^3)\}$ is a null sequence, by the Multiple Rule, so $\{a_n\}$ converges to $\frac{1}{2}$.

3.3 In each case we apply Strategy 3.1.

(a) The dominant term is n^3, so we write
$$a_n = \frac{n^3 + 2n^2 + 3}{2n^3 + 1} = \frac{1 + 2/n + 3/n^3}{2 + 1/n^3}.$$
Since $\{1/n\}$ and $\{1/n^3\}$ are basic null sequences,
$$\lim_{n\to\infty} a_n = \lim_{n\to\infty} \frac{1 + 2/n + 3/n^3}{2 + 1/n^3} = \frac{1+0+0}{2+0} = \tfrac{1}{2},$$
by the Combination Rules.

(b) The dominant term is 3^n, so we write
$$a_n = \frac{n^2 + 2^n}{3^n + n^3} = \frac{n^2/3^n + (2/3)^n}{1 + n^3/3^n}.$$
Since $\{n^2/3^n\} = \{n^2(1/3)^n\}, \{(2/3)^n\}$ and $\{n^3/3^n\} = \{n^3(1/3)^n\}$ are basic null sequences,
$$\lim_{n\to\infty} a_n = \lim_{n\to\infty} \frac{n^2/3^n + (2/3)^n}{1 + n^3/3^n} = \frac{0+0}{1+0} = 0,$$
by the Combination Rules.

(c) The dominant term is $n!$, so we write
$$a_n = \frac{n! + (-1)^n}{2^n + 3n!} = \frac{1 + (-1)^n/n!}{2^n/n! + 3}.$$
Since $\{(-1)^n/n!\}$ and $\{2^n/n!\}$ are basic null sequences,
$$\lim_{n\to\infty} a_n = \lim_{n\to\infty} \frac{1 + (-1)^n/n!}{2^n/n! + 3} = \frac{1+0}{0+3} = \tfrac{1}{3},$$
by the Combination Rules.

3.4 (a) By the rules for inequalities,
$$n^{1/n} \le 1 + \sqrt{\frac{2}{n-1}} \iff n \le \left(1 + \sqrt{\frac{2}{n-1}}\right)^n.$$
Using the hint with $x = \sqrt{2/(n-1)}$, we obtain
$$\left(1 + \sqrt{\frac{2}{n-1}}\right)^n \ge \frac{n(n-1)}{2!}\left(\sqrt{\frac{2}{n-1}}\right)^2$$
$$= \frac{n(n-1)}{2}\frac{2}{n-1} = n,$$
which gives the required inequality, for $n \ge 2$.

(b) Since $n \ge 1$, we have $n^{1/n} \ge 1$. Combining this inequality with that in part (a), we obtain
$$1 \le n^{1/n} \le 1 + \sqrt{\frac{2}{n-1}}, \quad \text{for } n \ge 2.$$
Now $\left\{\sqrt{\dfrac{2}{n-1}}\right\}_2^\infty$ is a null sequence, by the Multiple Rule and the Power Rule, so
$$\lim_{n\to\infty}\left(1 + \sqrt{\frac{2}{n-1}}\right) = 1.$$
Thus, by the Squeeze Rule,
$$\lim_{n\to\infty} n^{1/n} = 1.$$

3.5 (a) We have
$$a_n - 1 = \frac{n-1}{n+3} - 1 = \frac{-4}{n+3}.$$
Now $\left\{\dfrac{-4}{n+3}\right\}$ is a null sequence, by the Squeeze Rule, since
$$0 \le \left|\frac{-4}{n+3}\right| = \frac{4}{n+3} \le \frac{4}{n}, \quad \text{for } n = 1, 2, \ldots.$$
Thus $\{a_n\}$ is convergent with limit 1.

(b) We have
$$a_n - 1 = \frac{n^2}{n^2+n+1} - 1 = -\frac{n+1}{n^2+n+1}.$$
Now $\left\{-\dfrac{n+1}{n^2+n+1}\right\}$ is a null sequence, by the Squeeze Rule, since
$$0 \le \frac{n+1}{n^2+n+1} \le \frac{1}{n}, \quad \text{for } n = 1, 2, \ldots.$$
Thus $\{a_n\}$ is convergent with limit 1.

3.6 In each case we apply Strategy 3.1.

(a) The dominant term is n^2, so we write

$$\frac{n^2}{n^2+n+1} = \frac{1}{1+1/n+1/n^2}.$$

Since $\{1/n\}$ and $\{1/n^2\}$ are basic null sequences,

$$\lim_{n\to\infty} \frac{n^2}{n^2+n+1} = \lim_{n\to\infty} \frac{1}{1+1/n+1/n^2}$$
$$= \frac{1}{1+0+0} = 1,$$

by the Combination Rules.

(b) The dominant term is 2^n so we write

$$\frac{n^2-2^n}{2^n+n^{20}} = \frac{n^2/2^n-1}{1+n^{20}/2^n}.$$

Since $\{n^2/2^n\} = \{n^2(\frac{1}{2})^n\}$ and
$\{n^{20}/2^n\} = \{n^{20}(\frac{1}{2})^n\}$ are basic null sequences,

$$\lim_{n\to\infty} \frac{n^2-2^n}{2^n+n^{20}} = \lim_{n\to\infty} \frac{n^2/2^n-1}{1+n^{20}/2^n}$$
$$= \frac{0-1}{1+0} = -1,$$

by the Combination Rules.

(c) The dominant term is $n!$, so we write

$$\frac{5n!+5^n}{n^{100}+n!} = \frac{5+5^n/n!}{n^{100}/n!+1}.$$

Since $\{5^n/n!\}$ and $\{n^{100}/n!\}$ are basic null sequences,

$$\lim_{n\to\infty} \frac{5n!+5^n}{n^{100}+n!} = \lim_{n\to\infty} \frac{5+5^n/n!}{n^{100}/n!+1}$$
$$= \frac{5+0}{0+1} = 5,$$

by the Combination Rules.

3.7 The result follows from the Product Rule with $b_n = a_n$, for $n = 1, 2, \ldots$.

4.1 (a) The sequence $\{1+(-1)^n\}$ is bounded because $1+(-1)^n$ takes only the values 0 and 2, so

$$|1+(-1)^n| \le 2, \quad \text{for } n = 1, 2, \ldots.$$

(b) The sequence $\{(-1)^n n\}$ is unbounded. Given any positive number K, there is a positive integer n such that $|(-1)^n n| = n > K$; for example, $n = [K]+1$.

(c) The sequence $\left\{\frac{2n+1}{n}\right\}$ is bounded because

$$\left|\frac{2n+1}{n}\right| = 2+\frac{1}{n} \le 3, \quad \text{for } n = 1, 2, \ldots.$$

4.2 (a) The sequence $\{\sqrt{n}\}$ is unbounded and hence divergent, by the corollary to Theorem 4.1.

(b) The sequence $\left\{\frac{n^2+n}{n^2+1}\right\}$ is convergent (with limit 1) and hence bounded, by Theorem 4.1. In fact,

$$\frac{n^2+n}{n^2+1} \le \frac{n^2+n^2}{n^2} = 2, \quad \text{for } n = 1, 2, \ldots.$$

(c) The sequence $\{(-1)^n n^2\}$ is unbounded and hence divergent, by the corollary to Theorem 4.1.

(d) The terms of the sequence $\{n^{(-1)^n}\}$ are

$$1, 2, \tfrac{1}{3}, 4, \tfrac{1}{5}, 6, \ldots.$$

The sequence is unbounded because, given any positive number K, there is an even integer $2n$ such that $(2n)^{(-1)^{2n}} = 2n > K$. Hence the sequence is divergent, by the corollary to Theorem 4.1.

4.3 (a) Each term of $\{2^n/n\}$ is positive and $\{n/2^n\}$ is a basic null sequence.

Hence $2^n/n \to \infty$, by the Reciprocal Rule.

(b) The dominant term is 2^n, so we first write

$$2^n - n^9 = 2^n\left(1-\frac{n^9}{2^n}\right), \quad \text{for } n = 1, 2, \ldots.$$

Since $\{n^9/2^n\}$ is a basic null sequence, it follows that $\{n^9/2^n\}$ is eventually less than 1, so $\{2^n - n^9\}$ is eventually positive.

Next we write

$$\frac{1}{2^n - n^9} = \frac{1/2^n}{1-n^9/2^n}.$$

Now $\{1/2^n\}$ and $\{n^9/2^n\}$ are basic null sequences, so, by the Combination Rules,

$$\lim_{n\to\infty} \frac{1}{2^n - n^9} = \lim_{n\to\infty} \frac{1/2^n}{1-n^9/2^n}$$
$$= \frac{0}{1-0} = 0.$$

Hence $2^n - n^9 \to \infty$, by the Reciprocal Rule.

(c) We know that $2^n/n \to \infty$, by part (a), and

$$2^n/n + 5n^9 \ge 2^n/n, \quad \text{for } n = 1, 2, \ldots.$$

Hence $2^n/n + 5n^9 \to \infty$, by the Squeeze Rule.

(Alternatively, you could have used the Reciprocal Rule or the Sum and the Multiple Rules.)

(d) Each term of $\left\{\frac{2^n+n^2}{n^9+n}\right\}$ is positive and

$$\left(\frac{2^n+n^2}{n^9+n}\right)^{-1} = \frac{n^9+n}{2^n+n^2}.$$

The dominant term is 2^n, so we write

$$\frac{n^9+n}{2^n+n^2} = \frac{n^9/2^n+n/2^n}{1+n^2/2^n}.$$

Now $\{n/2^n\}$, $\{n^2/2^n\}$ and $\{n^9/2^n\}$ are basic null sequences, so

$$\lim_{n\to\infty} \frac{n^9+n}{2^n+n^2} = \lim_{n\to\infty} \frac{n^9/2^n+n/2^n}{1+n^2/2^n}$$
$$= \frac{0+0}{1+0} = 0,$$

by the Combination Rules.

Hence $\frac{2^n+n^2}{n^9+n} \to \infty$, by the Reciprocal Rule.

4.4 (a) (i) $a_2 = 4$, $a_4 = 16$, $a_6 = 36$, $a_8 = 64$, $a_{10} = 100$.

(ii) $a_3 = 9$, $a_7 = 49$, $a_{11} = 121$, $a_{15} = 225$, $a_{19} = 361$.

(iii) $a_1 = 1$, $a_4 = 16$, $a_9 = 81$, $a_{16} = 256$, $a_{25} = 625$.

(b) $a_1 = 1$, $a_3 = \frac{1}{3}$, $a_5 = \frac{1}{5}$; $a_2 = 2$, $a_4 = 4$, $a_6 = 6$.

4.5 (a) If $a_n = (-1)^n + \dfrac{1}{n}$, $n = 1, 2, \ldots$, then

$$a_{2k} = 1 + \frac{1}{2k} \quad \text{and} \quad a_{2k-1} = -1 + \frac{1}{2k-1},$$

for $k = 1, 2, \ldots$. Thus

$$\lim_{k \to \infty} a_{2k} = 1, \quad \text{whereas} \quad \lim_{k \to \infty} a_{2k-1} = -1.$$

Hence $\{a_n\}$ is divergent, by the First Subsequence Rule.

(b) If $a_n = \frac{1}{3}n - [\frac{1}{3}n]$, $n = 1, 2, \ldots$, then

$$a_{3k} = k - [k] = 0$$

and

$$a_{3k+1} = k + \tfrac{1}{3} - [k + \tfrac{1}{3}] = \tfrac{1}{3},$$

for $k = 1, 2, \ldots$. Thus

$$\lim_{k \to \infty} a_{3k} = 0, \quad \text{whereas} \quad \lim_{k \to \infty} a_{3k+1} = \tfrac{1}{3}.$$

Hence $\{a_n\}$ is divergent, by the First Subsequence Rule.

(c) If $a_n = n \sin(\frac{1}{2}n\pi)$, $n = 1, 2, \ldots$, then

$$a_1 = 1, \ a_2 = 0, \ a_3 = -3, \ a_4 = 0, \ a_5 = 5, \ a_6 = 0, \ldots.$$

Now

$$a_{4k+1} = (4k+1)\sin(2k\pi + \tfrac{1}{2}\pi)$$
$$= 4k + 1,$$

for $k = 1, 2, \ldots$. Thus $a_{4k+1} \to \infty$ as $k \to \infty$. Hence $\{a_n\}$ is divergent, by the Second Subsequence Rule.

4.6 (a) The sequence $\{n^{1/4}\}$ is unbounded and hence divergent, by the corollary to Theorem 4.1.

(b) The sequence $\{100^n/n!\}$ is a basic null sequence. Hence it is convergent and therefore bounded, by Theorem 4.1.

4.7 (a) Each term of $\{n!/n^3\}$ is positive and $\{n^3/n!\}$ is a basic null sequence.

Hence $n!/n^3 \to \infty$, by the Reciprocal Rule.

(b) Each term of $\{n^2 + 2n\}$ is positive and

$$0 \le \frac{1}{n^2 + 2n} \le \frac{1}{n^2}, \quad \text{for } n = 1, 2, \ldots.$$

Thus $\left\{\dfrac{1}{n^2 + 2n}\right\}$ is null, by the Squeeze Rule.

Hence $n^2 + 2n \to \infty$, by the Reciprocal Rule.

(c) The dominant term is n^2, so we first write

$$n^2 - 2n = n^2(1 - 2/n).$$

Since $2/n < 1$, for $n > 2$, we deduce that $\{n^2 - 2n\}$ is eventually positive.

Next we write

$$\frac{1}{n^2 - 2n} = \frac{1/n^2}{1 - 2/n}.$$

Now $\{1/n\}$ and $\{1/n^2\}$ are basic null sequences. Thus, by the Combination Rules,

$$\lim_{n \to \infty} \frac{1}{n^2 - 2n} = \lim_{n \to \infty} \frac{1/n^2}{1 - 2/n} = \frac{0}{1 - 0} = 0.$$

Hence $n^2 - 2n \to \infty$, by the Reciprocal Rule.

(d) The dominant term is $n!$, so we first write

$$n! - n^3 - 3^n = n!\left(1 - \frac{n^3}{n!} - \frac{3^n}{n!}\right).$$

Since $\{n^3/n!\}$ and $\{3^n/n!\}$ are basic null sequences, we know that there is some integer N such that

$$\frac{n^3}{n!} + \frac{3^n}{n!} < 1, \quad \text{for } n > N.$$

Thus $\{n! - n^3 - 3^n\}$ is eventually positive.

Next we write

$$\frac{1}{n! - n^3 - 3^n} = \frac{1/n!}{1 - n^3/n! - 3^n/n!}.$$

Now $\{1/n!\}$, $\{n^3/n!\}$ and $\{3^n/n!\}$ are basic null sequences. Thus, by the Combination Rules,

$$\lim_{n \to \infty} \frac{1}{n! - n^3 - 3^n} = \lim_{n \to \infty} \frac{1/n!}{1 - n^3/n! - 3^n/n!}$$
$$= \frac{0}{1 - 0 - 0} = 0.$$

Hence $n! - n^3 - 3^n \to \infty$, by the Reciprocal Rule.

4.8 (a) If $a_n = (-1)^n 2^n$, $n = 1, 2, \ldots$, then

$$a_{2k} = 2^{2k} = 4^k, \quad \text{for } k = 1, 2, \ldots.$$

Thus $a_{2k} \to \infty$, by the Reciprocal Rule, since $\{1/4^k\} = \{(1/4)^k\}$ is a basic null sequence with positive terms.

Hence $\{a_n\}$ is divergent, by the Second Subsequence Rule.

(b) If $a_n = \dfrac{(-1)^n n^2}{2n^2 + 1}$, $n = 1, 2, \ldots$, then

$$a_{2k} = \frac{(2k)^2}{2(2k)^2 + 1} = \frac{4k^2}{8k^2 + 1}$$

and

$$a_{2k-1} = \frac{-(2k-1)^2}{2(2k-1)^2 + 1} = -\frac{4k^2 - 4k + 1}{8k^2 - 8k + 3}.$$

The dominant term is k^2 in both cases, so

$$\lim_{k \to \infty} a_{2k} = \tfrac{1}{2}, \quad \text{whereas} \quad \lim_{k \to \infty} a_{2k-1} = -\tfrac{1}{2},$$

by the Combination Rules.

Hence $\{a_n\}$ is divergent, by the First Subsequence Rule.

5.1 We use the following formulas.

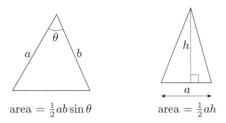

area $= \frac{1}{2}ab\sin\theta$ area $= \frac{1}{2}ah$

(a) Area $= \frac{1}{2} \times 1 \times 1 \times \sin\left(\frac{1}{3}\pi\right) = \frac{1}{2} \times \frac{\sqrt{3}}{2} = \frac{\sqrt{3}}{4}$.

(b) Area $= \frac{1}{2} \times 1 \times 1 \times \sin\left(\frac{1}{6}\pi\right) = \frac{1}{2} \times \frac{1}{2} = \frac{1}{4}$.

(c) Area $= \frac{1}{2} \times 2\tan\left(\frac{1}{6}\pi\right) \times 1 = \frac{1}{2} \times 2 \times \frac{1}{\sqrt{3}} = \frac{1}{\sqrt{3}}$.

(d) Area $= \frac{1}{2} \times 2\tan\left(\frac{1}{12}\pi\right) \times 1 = \tan\left(\frac{1}{12}\pi\right)$.

To find $\tan(\frac{1}{12}\pi)$, we use the formula

$$\tan\left(\tfrac{1}{6}\pi\right) = \frac{2\tan\left(\frac{1}{12}\pi\right)}{1 - \tan^2\left(\frac{1}{12}\pi\right)}.$$

Since $\tan\left(\frac{1}{6}\pi\right) = 1/\sqrt{3}$, we obtain

$$\tan^2\left(\tfrac{1}{12}\pi\right) + 2\sqrt{3}\tan\left(\tfrac{1}{12}\pi\right) - 1 = 0,$$

so

$$\tan\left(\tfrac{1}{12}\pi\right) = \frac{-2\sqrt{3} \pm \sqrt{(2\sqrt{3})^2 + 4}}{2}$$

$$= -\sqrt{3} \pm 2.$$

Because $\tan\left(\frac{1}{12}\pi\right) > 0$, we must have $\tan\left(\frac{1}{12}\pi\right) = 2 - \sqrt{3}$, so the area is $2 - \sqrt{3}$.

5.2 (a) The Binomial Theorem gives

$$\left(1 + \frac{x}{n}\right)^n$$

$$= 1 + n\left(\frac{x}{n}\right) + \frac{n(n-1)}{2!}\left(\frac{x}{n}\right)^2 + \cdots + \left(\frac{x}{n}\right)^n$$

$$= 1 + x + \frac{1}{2!}\left(1 - \frac{1}{n}\right)x^2 + \cdots + \frac{x^n}{n^n}.$$

The $(k+1)$th term in this sum is

$$\frac{n(n-1)\cdots(n-k+1)}{k!}\left(\frac{x}{n}\right)^k$$

$$= \frac{1}{k!}\left(1 - \frac{1}{n}\right)\left(1 - \frac{2}{n}\right)\cdots\left(1 - \frac{k-1}{n}\right)x^k.$$

If k and x are fixed, then this term increases as n increases, for $n \geq k$. Hence the sequence $\{(1 + x/n)^n\}$ is increasing if $x > 0$.

(b) To prove that $\{(1 + x/n)^n\}$ is bounded above, we choose an integer $k \geq x$ and use the inequality in the hint:

$$\left(1 + \frac{x}{n}\right)^n \leq \left(1 + \frac{k}{n}\right)^n$$

$$\leq \left(\left(1 + \frac{1}{n}\right)^k\right)^n$$

$$= \left(\left(1 + \frac{1}{n}\right)^n\right)^k \leq e^k,$$

since the sequence $\{(1 + 1/n)^n\}$ is increasing with limit e. Hence $\{(1 + x/n)^n\}$ is bounded above by e^k.

(c) As the sequence $\{(1 + x/n)^n\}$ is increasing and bounded above, it must be convergent, by the Monotone Convergence Theorem.

5.3 We know, from Exercise 5.2 (with $x = \frac{3}{2}$), that $\{(1 + (3/2)/n)^n\}$ is convergent. Suppose that

$$\lim_{n\to\infty}\left(1 + \frac{3/2}{n}\right)^n = \lim_{n\to\infty}\left(1 + \frac{3}{2n}\right)^n = \alpha.$$

Then, by the Product Rule,

$$\lim_{n\to\infty}\left(1 + \frac{3}{2n}\right)^{2n} = \alpha^2. \qquad\qquad (\text{S.1})$$

Now, the sequence in equation (S.1) is a subsequence of $\{(1 + 3/n)^n\}$ and we know that $\{(1 + 3/n)^n\}$ is convergent with limit e^3. Hence, by Theorem 4.2(a),

$$\alpha^2 = e^3,$$

so

$$\lim_{n\to\infty}\left(1 + \frac{3/2}{n}\right)^n = \alpha = e^{3/2}.$$

5.4 By the Monotonic Sequence Theorem,

EITHER $\{a_n\}$ is convergent,

OR $a_n \to \infty$.

If $a_n \to \infty$ as $n \to \infty$, then it follows from Theorem 4.2(b) that $a_{n_k} \to \infty$ as $k \to \infty$, and we know that this is false.

Hence $\{a_n\}$ must be convergent.

5.5 The first n terms of the sequence $\{(1 + 1/n)^n\}$ are

$$\left(\frac{2}{1}\right)^1, \left(\frac{3}{2}\right)^2, \left(\frac{4}{3}\right)^3, \ldots, \left(\frac{n+1}{n}\right)^n.$$

Taking the product of these terms, each of which is less than e, we obtain

$$\frac{2^1\,3^2\,4^3\,\cdots\,(n+1)^n}{1^1\,2^2\,3^3\,\cdots\,n^n} < e^n.$$

By cancelling common factors in this quotient, we obtain

$$\frac{(n+1)^n}{n!} < e^n.$$

Hence

$$n! > \frac{(n+1)^n}{e^n} = \left(\frac{n+1}{e}\right)^n, \qquad \text{for } n = 1, 2, \ldots,$$

as required.

Index

Archimedean algorithm, 41

basic null sequence, 17, 20
bounded above, 38
bounded below, 38
bounded sequence, 30

Combination Rules, 14, 24, 34
constant sequence, 7, 22, 25
convergent sequence, 22–29, 31

decreasing sequence, 7
    strategies, 8
divergent sequence, 30–37
    definition, 30
    strategy, 36
dominant term, 24

e, 42–44
even subsequence, 35
eventually, 9–10

First Subsequence Rule, 36

increasing sequence, 7
    strategies, 8

limit, 22
Limit Inequality Rule, 28

Monotone Convergence Theorem, 38–44
monotonic sequence, 7
Monotonic Sequence Theorem, 39

Multiple Rule, 14, 19, 24, 34

non-convergent sequence, *see* divergent sequence
nth term, 5
null sequence, 10–21
    basic, 17, 20
    definition, 12, 18
    strategy, 13

odd subsequence, 35

π, 40–42
Power Rule, 14, 18
Product Rule, 14, 19, 24, 25, 34

Quotient Rule, 24, 26

Reciprocal Rule, 33

Second Subsequence Rule, 36
sequence, 5
sequence diagram, 6
Squeeze Rule, 15, 16, 27, 34
strictly decreasing sequence, 7
strictly increasing sequence, 7
subsequence, 35–37
Subsequence Rules, 36
Sum Rule, 14, 19, 24, 25, 34

tends to infinity, 32–34

unbounded sequence, 30